GALILEO IN CHINA

GALILEO IN CHINA

Relations through the Roman College
between Galileo and the
Jesuit Scientist-Missionaries (1610–1640)

by *PASQUALE M. D'ELIA, S. J.*

Professor of Sinology at the Pontifical Gregorian University
and at the State University of Rome

Translated by

Rufus SUTER and Matthew SCIASCIA

Foreword by Donald H. Menzel

HARVARD UNIVERSITY PRESS
Cambridge, Massachusetts 1960

PREFACE

In 1942 the tercentenary of the death of Galileo Galilei (1564–1642) occurred. In Italy, the land of his birth, several cultural organizations believed that this event should be observed in spite of the belligerency in the air. Among these organizations were the Royal Academy of Italy and the Pontifical Gregorian University.

The former, then in full operation, thought that the best way to commemorate Galileo was to invite a score of scholars especially competent in this subject matter to lecture on him and his discoveries at the seat of the Academy, the Farnese Palace. Among the topics chosen for discussion was that of the rapid spread of knowledge of his discoveries to the Far East, and in particular to China, where in those days Jesuit missionaries were engaged in a scientific apostolate rarely equaled in the history of Catholic missions. The Academy, therefore, invited me to lecture on "Echoes of Galileo's Discoveries in China,"[1] and I had the opportunity to study the unexpected zeal of these same missionaries in their efforts to understand, verify, adopt, and publish abroad the discoveries of the great Tuscan. My investigations were conducted chiefly in unpublished documents and Chinese sources untranslated into any European language. They bore a rich harvest. I limited myself to the period before the scientist's death, a restriction which sharpened still further the interest of the theme. My lecture was given on March 28, 1942, before a select audience at the Farnese Palace.

The Pontifical Gregorian University also wished to commemorate this tercentenary. It was mindful of the ready support which the professors of the Roman College, its direct ancestor, gave the Pisan astronomer's discoveries. It was mindful that a celebrated professor of mathematics at the Roman College, the Bavarian Christopher Clavius (or Klau), known for the reform of the Gregorian Calendar, confirmed Galileo's discoveries. Clavius also supported the Pisan's Copernican interpretation, and, because of the immense prestige he enjoyed among the learned, he was responsible for their relatively prompt acceptance in learned circles. The Gregorian University, finally, was mindful that in May 1611 the Roman College received Galileo within its walls, and honored him with a solemn convocation. Although he was only at the beginning of his fame, he was introduced at this gathering by a friend of Clavius as one of the most celebrated and fortunate astronomers of the age. The Pontifical Gregorian University, therefore, asked me to lecture on "Galileo and the Society of Jesus: From Roman College to Far East."[2] This lecture was given on April 26, 1942.

Thus, I have traced the spread of the knowledge of Galileo's discoveries with the Roman College as the point of departure.

Here in summary are the results of my research:

Matthew Ricci died at Peking on May 11, 1610, insisting that his superiors send him an astronomer. A few days earlier Galileo announced his discoveries to the world in his *Sidereal Messenger*.[3] From November 28, 1610, until April 6, 1611, professors at the Roman College confirmed Galileo's discoveries by their own observations and became ardent defenders. In May 1611, Galileo was honored by the convocation at the Roman College. Clavius before his death (February 6, 1612) announced in a publication of 1611 that Galileo's discoveries made it necessary to modify the ancient Ptolemaic position and to adopt the heliocentric system of Copernicus. News of Galileo's discoveries was immediately communicated to Jesuit missionaries in India, reaching them in 1612 or shortly thereafter. From India the news spread to China with a rapidity remarkable for those days. It first came to the attention of the Chinese in 1615 on the last page of a book by a Jesuit missionary which had just come off the press. Galileo was appointed to membership in the Academy of the Lincei on April 25, 1611. He was the sixth member, and the seventh, appointed eight days later, was John Schreck, or Terrentius, who the following November 1 entered the Society of Jesus and a few years later embarked for China in response to the urgent requests for astronomical help. In place of Gregory of St. Vincent, Christopher Scheiner, Galileo's antagonist, and John Cysat, who had offered to go to China but had been recalled, the Jesuits who actually sailed for the Middle Kingdom in 1618 in response to the repeated calls were the Italian James Rho, the Bohemian Wenceslaus Kirwitzer, the Austrian John Alberich, the German John

Adam Schall von Bell, and the Swiss John Schreck, mentioned above. Schreck before and after his arrival in China wrote frequently to Italy begging Galileo to aid the missionary-scientists in their efforts to correct the Chinese calendar, which had been in error for several centuries. This request Galileo finally refused, probably because of a quarrel with two Jesuits, Horace Grassi and Christopher Scheiner. The missionary-scientists, therefore, turned to Kepler for help, and he, as if to compensate for Galileo, replied immediately and in detail to all the questions of the Jesuit scientists.

They did not, however, forget the great Italian. Instead they brought the telescope and the astronomical discoveries made by means of it to the attention of educated Chinese. They published a treatise on the telescope in 1626. Schreck, two years before his death, cited his friend's discoveries in a Chinese book (c. 1628). From the Middle Kingdom news of the discoveries was carried to Korea in 1631 and then to Japan before 1638. In 1634 a telescope was explained and presented to the emperor of China. The same year Schall printed two Chinese works in which the Pisan's discoveries were again mentioned. Finally, in 1640, or shortly before, the missionaries introduced Galileo's name to the Chinese in their characters, 加利勒阿 (Chia-li-lê-o), and praised him for having reached where "no other astronomer had reached in several thousand years."

This zeal with which the Jesuits made Galileo's discoveries known in China, Korea, and Japan, while the astronomer was yet alive, suggests that they might have followed him in his heliocentric conclusions had it not been for the injunction of 1616 and especially the sentence of 1633. They probably were Copernicans at heart, but the judgment of higher authority made it impossible for them to teach the heliocentric system in their scientific publications in the Chinese language.

The documents upon which the following study is based open a new and unexpected page in the history of science. This is why I have felt it worthwhile to continue my investigations, though confining them to the period before the great astronomer's death, and to combine and complete my two lectures before the Royal Academy of Italy and Pontifical Gregorian University.

Originally the lecture before the Royal Academy was to be published in a large volume of *Galileian Studies*.[4] The type had even been composed. But then, as is common knowledge, grave disaster fell upon beloved Italy, and the Royal Academy, involved in the accumulated material, moral, and cultural ruin, was destroyed—a catastrophe which was very tragic to all who were accustomed to see in that organization the intellectual senate of the nation.

Subsequently, when the National Academy of the Lincei was revived to carry on the cultural tradition of the suppressed Royal Academy, the first part of my work on Galileo was published in its *Acts*.[5] Since, however, these *Acts* are not easily available, I published an enlarged version of my work in the series *Analecta Gregoriana*[6] of the Pontifical Gregorian University. The additional material is an appendix containing a document hitherto unpublished in a Western language, on the correction of the Chinese calendar. This document, the earliest on the subject, is by a companion and disciple of Ricci who was in correspondence with Christopher Grienberger, Clavius' successor at the Roman College. It is dated September 1, 1612, a little more than a year after Ricci's death. Drawn up by a scientist, it shows immediately the difficulty of the work the Chinese asked of the missionary-scientists in reforming their calendar and why Schreck pressed Galileo so insistently for his aid.

May this modest essay dissipate the last clouds in the Galilean sky and show us once more that science and faith are sisters, daughters of the same Eternal Wisdom.

PASQUALE M. D'ELIA, S.J.

Rome, February 2, 1947

CONTENTS

APPENDIX

The First European Document on the Chinese Calendar (August
1612) Report of Father Sabatino De Ursis, S.J., to Father Francis
Pasio, S.J., on the Chinese Calendar   61

ILLUSTRATIONS

FOREWORD
by
Donald H. Menzel

Galileo in China is a fascinating excerpt from the history of science, depicting the impact of Galileo on the Far East and showing how his theories and his telescope influenced human thought during the scientist's lifetime. The book paints an interesting picture of Chinese astronomy, as practiced over the centuries. It also throws new light on the famous conflict between Galileo and the church. Old Chinese sources dating from the period 1610–1640, furnish most of the background data.

Galileo, of course, did not visit China himself. Jesuit missionaries, faced with hostile reception of their religious doctrines, sought to win friends by teaching science, chiefly mathematics and astronomy.

The Chinese calendar was then in an almost hopeless state of confusion. Some authorities blamed this condition upon the loss of rules for its construction when an emperor ordered the destruction of all books in the year 213 B.C. Since most of the books were recovered at a later date, however, the real reason for the confusion of the calendar appears to have been imperfections in the basic rules and a lack of proper observational means for revising them.

The Chinese calendar, like many other important ones of antiquity, was one of the luni-solar variety. It tried somehow to reconcile the inequalities of the lunar month and the solar year. The interval between successive full moons is nearly $29\frac{1}{2}$ days. By alternating months of 30 days with those of 29 days, one can, therefore, keep the calendar roughly in agreement with the lunar phases. But 12 such months contain only 354 days, 11 less than that of the normal solar year of 365 days. Over 19 years, the discrepancy amounts to 209 days, which can be divided into six months of 30 days and one of 29. These are inserted into the calendar at stated intervals, to equalize the lunar and solar years.

The foregoing procedure is unduly simplified. First of all, the solar year is not 365 but 365.2422 days in length. We may compensate for this fact, in the purely solar calendar, by intercalating a leap day every four years, except for the century years not divisible by 400. Thus the chance of any given year's having an extra day is $\frac{1}{4}$ minus $\frac{3}{400}$ or 0.2500–0.0075=0.2425, a good approximation to the decimal given above, 0.2422. Thus, in 19 years, the number of extra days averages to 19×0.2425 or 4.6075. This rounds off to either 4 or 5 whole days, which are then added to the extra lunar months of 29 days as needed.

The total number of days is 19×354+30×6+29+4.6075=6939.6075 days in all, to be divided among 19×12+6+1=235 lunar months. The average number of days per lunar month, therefore, comes out 29.5302. This number agrees closely with the actual observed interval of 29.5306 days between successive full moons.

This correspondence comes about by pure chance. It means that, over a considerable period of time, the phases of the moon tend to recur in a cycle of nineteen years. In consequence, the problem of predicting the lunar phases is greatly simplified. Meton discovered the basic fact in 432 B.C. that 19 solar years contain 235 lunations. In A.D. 325 the Nicene council further developed the Metonic cycle, applying it to the calculation of ecclesiastical events.

As a result of the widespread knowledge of the cycle it is surprising that the Chinese apparently were ignorant of its advantages. They probably preferred not to have a perpetual calendar. Every year they re-calculated it on a day-to-day basis. Eclipses, which held special significance for the Chinese, gave them the greatest trouble. For example, the imperial astronomers had erred by a half hour in their prediction of the eclipse of December 15, 1610.

In their confusion the Chinese called on the Jesuits for assistance. They, in turn, appealed to their superiors in Rome for books and information. They repeatedly asked that a father skilled in astronomy and mathematics be sent to China to help in the work. But communication was difficult and the project lagged.

News of Galileo's telescope and his discoveries with it inspired some of the Jesuits to copy his instrument and make their own observations. Thus they confirmed many of his findings and independently drew similar conclusions. Even though the injunction of 1616 deterred them from accepting the heliocentric theory, they nevertheless came to believe that Venus was a satellite of the sun, rather than of the earth.

Numerous direct appeals to Galileo for information about methods of calculating eclipses completely failed. The personal dispute between him and the Jesuits evidently led the Tuscan astronomer to remain silent. It was Kepler who finally furnished the desired data, which enabled the Jesuits, at long last, to complete the revision of the calendar, more than 25 years after the original request went in to Rome from Father Ricci.

It seems ironic that the Chinese, for all their vaunted erudition, were not up to the task of revising the calendar and had to depend on the Jesuits for this task. And, even though Galileo did not contribute personally to the effort, the record is clear that his observations and discoveries had a profound and lasting effect on Far Eastern culture, despite the difficulties that he personally suffered in Italy.

Galileo in China is a thoughtful translation of significant records, sympathetically annotated by the author. Suter and Sciascia have produced a highly readable and interesting rendition into English of the original Italian lectures given by Pasquale M. D'Elia, S.J.

GALILEO IN CHINA

TRANSLATORS' NOTE

Romanization of Chinese characters is according to the system used in the H. A. Giles Chinese-English Dictionary. Geographical place names in China have, however, usually been given the conventional English spellings instead of the Wade-Giles romanization. Their characters have been omitted. The romanization of Chinese book titles has been supplied for the convenience of readers who may want to find the titles in a romanized library catalog.

In most cases passages in foreign languages have been removed from the text proper of this work and included in the footnotes. This leaves the text almost entirely in English, with the passages which were originally in foreign languages translated into English. Thus, the longer Chinese passages (except one) have been removed to the footnotes, leaving only the translation in the text proper. Christian names have been given their English form when there is one. This was the regular policy in the Italian edition (with the tables turned, of course). English translations of book titles have been given in the text proper, with the original book titles in the footnotes, usually.

The Portuguese column in the Appendix has been omitted.

Anything enclosed in brackets [ ] has been supplied by the translators. Anything enclosed in braces { } is editorial comment that D'Elia had placed in brackets or had indicated by asterisks*.

In addition to a number of small changes and corrections, Father D'Elia has supplied for this translation new material for chapters 23, 26, 27, and 28 and the whole of chapter 30.

If glory is, according to St. Augustine's classical definition, "clara cum laude notitia"—clear and deserved knowledge of a person's merits—it will be the greater the farther this knowledge reaches and the more rapid its diffusion in time and space.

That knowledge of Galileo's merits has been affirmed more and more with the passage of time all see, because the matter is so evident. That his discoveries were quickly recognized and appreciated in the learned world in Italy and Europe, notwithstanding contradictions and struggles, this is not the place to prove. But that these discoveries reached the extreme limits of the then known world—China, Korea, and even Japan—and that in an age when communication between Italy and such distant countries was rare and difficult, and in a relatively short period of time, this perhaps is less known in our Western world, and, if it is supported by indisputable proofs, will increase not a little the glory of the great Italian scientist. These proofs can really be adduced. They are supplied us by European sources, often unpublished,[1] and—what is practically the same as being unpublished —by rare Chinese sources never published in any European language,[2] and here translated for the first time. . . .[3]

1. *China Before Matthew Ricci*

Galileo's birth in 1564 marked the twelfth year since the death of the indefatigable Francis Xavier, whose end came on the rock of Shangch'uan 上川 at the gates of China, a land almost unknown in those days in Europe because it had been closed to foreigners for about two centuries. Since the time of Marco Polo fantastic legends circulated about Cathay and China, whose southern ports were reached fifty years before [Galileo's birth] by intrepid Portuguese sailors. The people of Europe still thought that Cathay and China were two separate countries: Cathay in the north, named by the medieval Venetian traveler; China in the south, reached by the Portuguese caravels. The capital of

Cathay was Cambaluc;[4] the capital of China, Peking. Nobody guessed that the two countries and the two cities were identical. Cosmologists and geographers perpetuated these and many other errors about that far edge of eastern Asia.

After the sailors came the heroic missionaries, whose movement to China was determined precisely by the death of Xavier. Between the date of his death, 1552, and 1582, about sixty missionaries of various nationalities and orders knocked at the gates of China, mostly Franciscans and Jesuits, Spanish, Portuguese, and Italian. Some of them, with perseverance and indomitable courage, knocked more than once at the hermetically sealed gates, but in vain. They all presented themselves on the southern coast of China from where the more fortunate pushed on to Canton or the neighboring city of Shiuhing. But after a few weeks or months their ignorance of the language and customs forced them to turn back and to abandon their course.[5]

2. Matthew Ricci Opens the Gates of China

The honor of opening the Middle Kingdom—that area vaster than the whole of Europe—was reserved for Matthew Ricci of Macerata. Born in the year of Xavier's death, 1552, he studied first at his native place, then in Rome. He was intended originally for the law, but instead he joined the Society of Jesus when he was nineteen years old. After his novitiate he pursued a course of scholarly and scientific studies at the Roman College under the celebrated Father Clavius,[6] a great admirer, as we shall see, of Galileo. The sciences he learned at that time served him later as the key for penetration where all before him had suffered shipwreck. He left Rome in 1577, when Galileo was barely thirteen years old. He embarked from Lisbon for Goa, whither he arrived via the Cape of Good Hope in September 1578, after six months of dangerous and harsh sailing. India retained him about three years, then on April 15, 1582, at the order of that incomparably mighty figure among missionaries, Father Alexander Valignano, then superior of all Jesuit missions in the Middle and Far East,[7] he set sail for Macao to give an effective start to a Chinese mission. His first station, founded September 10, 1583, was at Shiuhing, the seat of the viceroy of the two coastal provinces, Kwangtung and Kwangsi. In succeeding years he pushed northward, founding four other stations: at Shiuchow, Kwangtung Province; at Nanchang, Kiangsi Province; at Nanking, the Southern Capital; and finally at Peking, the Northern Capital. He ended his days there on May 11, 1610, in the very year when the fame of the great Pisan astronomer was beginning.[8]

3. The Chinese Calendar

If Ricci was first tolerated, then esteemed, and finally loved in the Middle Kingdom, the reason was largely his method. This consisted in the application of science to the service of the Gospel. To Ricci is owed, as is recognized by all educated Chinese, the introduction to the Middle Kingdom of Occidental science. The very fact that he was permitted by the Chinese authorities to go to Peking was in part a result of the hope he fostered in the mandarins that he could correct the Chinese calendar, which had been mistaken for several centuries and no Chinese astronomer could correct. The calendar for the Chinese was an important political instrument; lands accepting it were considered vassals and tributaries to China; those rejecting it, on the other hand, were rebels and thus worthy of punishment. But the scientific rules upon which the calendar was based had been lost long ago, so that for years it was only compiled empirically, and therefore was not free of grave errors.

4. Send Me an Authentic Astronomer!

Ricci was not an astronomer. Though he occasionally busied himself with astronomical matters, he would have been the first to recognize that his science in this respect was very limited. He wrote on May 12, 1605, from Peking to his Roman superiors that he was doing some scientific work and some modest work in practical astronomy (probably on Andrew de Avelar's *Repertorio dos tempos*). He observed that, since he was able to do so much work acceptable to the Chinese with the meager means at his disposal, he certainly would be able to do far more if a competent astronomer were sent from Rome to Peking. In his own words: "These globes, clocks, spheres, astrolabes, and so forth, which I have made and the use of which I teach, have gained for me the reputation of being the greatest mathematician in the world. I do not have a single book on astrology,[9] but with only the help of certain ephemerides and Portuguese almanacs I sometimes predict eclipses more accurately than they do. For this reason, when I tell them that I have no books and that I do not wish to start to correct their rules, few people here believe me. And accordingly I say that, if the mathematician of whom I spoke came here, we could readily translate our tables into Chinese characters and rectify their year.[10] This would give us great face, would open wider the gates of China, and would enable us to live more securely and freely."[11]

In this same letter he requested, supplicated, and insisted that a great mathematician, an authentic astronomer, be sent him. Addressing the Assistant to the General in Rome in charge of the affairs of the Portuguese Province and Missions, he wrote: "I wish exceedingly to beg Your Reverence for something which for many years I have been asking, but without response. And that is that one of the most useful things which could come from there {Rome} to this court {of Peking} would be a father or even a brother who is a good astrologer,[12] who could draw up ephemerides." Since 1605 was "many years" after his unanswered request for an astronomer, it is likely that the original appeal was in about 1595, when a friend wished him "to correct the Chinese year which is in error."[13] In this same letter of 1605 Ricci explained that the Chinese emperor supported more than two hundred persons "at much expense" to make the annual calendar, and that it fairly swarmed with mistakes. The Chinese attach most significance, he related, to knowledge of the trajectory and position of the planets, and to the prediction of eclipses. He concluded: "I wish that Your Reverence would discuss this matter which is of such importance to China with our father {the General}, and that he would send one or two [astronomers], regardless of their nationality, directly to China, or better yet to Peking, as in the other parts they would be of little use." He added opportunely: "And see to it that he brings the necessary books."[14] How close this matter was to Ricci's heart is evident in his next to last letter sent from Peking, March 8, 1608, two years before his death, begging again that Rome send "a good mathematician, especially an astrologer."[15]

On December 12, 1599, Emmanuel Diaz also wrote from Macao to General Acquaviva that Cattaneo and the other fathers of the mission wanted a good mathematician.[16]

5. Galileo and Father Clavius

Meanwhile in Italy knowledge of the foundations of astronomy and related sciences was being renewed in these very years. Galileo's fame reached its pinnacle thanks to his ingenious discoveries. The friendship binding him to the celebrated Clavius was two decades old. One of his earliest letters, that of January 8, 1588, was to Clavius. In it the young scientist, still unknown, asked the professor at the Roman College about the demonstration of a problem in centers of gravity. First, however, he protested: "I prefer Your Reverend Lordship's judgment above that of any other. If you are silent, I shall be silent, too; if not, I shall turn to another demonstration."[17] Continuing the same discussion in a second letter, February 25, 1588, Galileo revealed all his thought to Clavius, excusing himself by saying: "I know that with friends of truth like Your Reverend Lordship one may and ought to speak freely."[18]

This ancient friendship had a rebirth and a rekindling in the last years of Clavius' long life. In July 1609, Galileo constructed what he called an "occhiale" and a "cannone," later known as a "cannocchiale,"[19] and later still as a "telescopio."[20] With this instrument began, in September of that year, the series of his discoveries: the phases of Venus, the "three-bodied" appearance of Saturn, the mountains on the moon, the many stars in the Pleiades and Milky Way, four of the moons of Jupiter, the nebula in Orion, the nebula in Praesepe. He announced these discoveries in March 1610, in his famous *Sidereal Messenger.*[21]

Excitement in the learned world was great. These sensational and unexpected discoveries that were destined to overthrow the whole Peripatetic system, which had been admitted by everybody in all the schools for centuries, aroused enthusiasm in some and suspicion in others. Clavius, who was more than seventy, felt rejuvenated by these discoveries. He wrote, probably to Anthony de' Medici, a letter of inquiry about the credibility of the reports. From his correspondent Clavius received a copy of a letter that Galileo had sent to de' Medici, thus accounting for its presence among the unpublished Clavian correspondence in the Archives of the Pontifical Gregorian University. Galileo, on January 7, 1610, described in detail to his friend his lunar observations: "To satisfy Your Most Illustrious Lordship, I shall recount briefly what I have seen through one of my telescopes on the face of the moon, which I have been able to bring, as it were, very near, that is, to within three earth-diameters. This telescope presents the diameter of the moon as being twenty times greater than it appears to the naked eye."[22]

6. Verification of the Discoveries at the Roman College

Clavius and his successor in the chair of mathematics at the Roman College, the Tyrolese Christopher Grienberger (1561–1636), did not, of course, let themselves be led by unthinking enthusiasm. First of all they wanted to verify personally the observations. Thus, aided by their pupils, from November 28, 1610, until April 6, 1611, they spent long nights scrutinizing the heavens to observe the four satellites of Jupiter.[23] Clavius, who had been rather "obstinate" about admitting Galileo's observations, on December 17, 1610 announced to Galileo that in Rome they saw "many times most distinctly" the four satellites of Jupiter and also that "very early" they observed "the numerous stars in the Pleiades, Cancer, Orion, and the Milky Way, invisible without the instrument." Saturn looked to them "oblong like this: oϽ·." The old professor of the Roman College then encouraged the young scientist to continue his researches: "perhaps you will find other new things on other planets." Referring specifically to the four satellites of Jupiter, Clavius remarked that Galileo deserved "great praise" for being the first to discover them.[24]

Naturally this news pleased the Pisan astronomer. On December 30, 1610, he replied to Clavius expressing joy for the letter, "as much appreciated as it was desired and little expected," bringing him "such testimony to the truth" of his observations. Indeed, the letter from Clavius delighted him so much that, though it found him in bed, he felt recovered from his sickness. Moreover it gained him sympathy in other quarters, although there were suspicious persons who insinuated that the letter of the highly esteemed Clavius was written to flatter the astronomer, or that its sentiments were downright pretended. In this same letter, Galileo also announced that he had observed Saturn again, "and that it looked exactly like ⌖," adding: "I have shown it so distinctly to many of your brothers here that they do not doubt." In conclusion the great scientist asked for Clavius' continuing esteem, as well as for the good wishes of his successor, Grienberger: "Excuse my delight in treating with you, and continue to grant me your grace, for which I supplicate you in every instance. Also gain for me the grace of the other, Father Christopher {Grienberger}, your disciple, whose reputation for mathematical ability has aroused my highest admiration."[25]

This last reflection induced Grienberger to write directly to Galileo a long Latin letter, dated January 22, 1611, in which he thanked the great astronomer for his compliments, and dwelt upon the difficulty of abandoning centuries-old, widely supported scientific beliefs. He described in detail his own observations, and concluded: "Certainly if I had not seen with my own eyes through the Roman instrument, and shown to some others, the wonders which you recently and for the first time introduced to the world, I doubt that I should have agreed with you yet. . . . Now Clavius and almost everybody in Rome who have observed the new phenomena grant your opinion, or, at least, they do not dissent so positively as before; I should be astonished to find anybody who, having seen what I have seen, would still not believe it."[26] He also communicated that on January 17 he had enjoyed the unusual experience of at the same time observing the moon with one unaided eye and Venus through the telescope with the other eye, and seeing them both at the same phase.

Even before either of these two letters, Galileo knew that Clavius had acknowledged to his disciples the truth of his discoveries. He learned it from Anthony Santini, to whom the professor at the Roman College wrote sometime before December 4, 1610, doubtless to thank him for the magnificent telescope he had sent from Venice, which enabled [Clavius] to make observations that had not been possible when an instrument of his own construction had proved inadequate. In fact, on December 4, 1610, Santini communicated to Galileo: "Finally, Father Clavius of Rome writes me how they have observed Jupiter."[27] On the same day that Clavius wrote to Galileo the letter cited above, that is to say, December 17, 1610, Galileo wrote to Paul Gualdo at Padua: "At last I can compare observations of the Medicean planets made by some Jesuit fathers, students of Father Clavius, and by Clavius himself, written down and sent also to Venice. I have often shown these [Medicean stars] to some of these same fathers here in Florence, both to those who live here and to those who pass through, and they make use of them in their sermons and orations with very gracious conceptions."[28]

After reassuring the discoverer, Clavius, whose authority in this field in those days was indisputable, reassured the discoverer's friends. One of these friends was Welser, a great philanthropist and a duumvir of Augsburg. Perplexed about the celestial novelties observed, on January 7, 1611, he asked the old professor of the Roman College to tell him frankly what he thought.[29]

We still possess, unpublished, Clavius' reply to Welser. Its purport is as follows: "Concerning Your Lordship's inquiry of January 7, I must say that I too was at one time doubtful about the Medicean stars, supposing that they were hallucinations produced by the telescope.[30] But now I no longer doubt, because here at the College we have seen these planets frequently mornings and evenings. I shall append some of my observations to this letter. It is true, however, that to see them one must have a perfect instrument, as is mine sent to me from Venice by a mathematician friend.[31] With this same telescope I have seen near Saturn two stars, one on either side, conjoined thus: ˚O˚. Moreover, I have seen Venus to be almost like the moon, with horns opposite the sun, a most remarkable sight, indicating that it takes its light from the sun. I believe that other strange phenomena will be observed in the planets. Your Lordship need no longer doubt these observations." At the end of the letter are Clavius' observations of November 14, December 16, and January 23, at 2 and 4 A.M. and 10 P.M., and finally of the evening of January 25. The letter ends with these words: "Venus three months ago was almost full. Then as it moved towards the left, away [from the sun], it began to grow horned like the waxing moon."[32]

Welser replied: "Your Reverence's letter satisfies me, and leaves me reassured and convinced of the miracles wrought by Mr. Galilei in the Jovian stars, Saturn, and Venus. Previously, I was skeptical in spite of his many assertions."[33]

Guido Bettoli of Perugia, on June 4, 1611, also sought advice from Clavius, Grienberger, and other fathers at the Roman College about Galileo's discoveries, and doubtless received the same reassuring replies.[34]

The full approval by Clavius and his pupils of the great astronomer's discoveries must have impressed the learned world not a little, since Ernest of Bavaria, prince-elector and archbishop of Cologne, felt the need of having a copy made of the above-cited letter from Clavius to Welser, and he sent it to Clavius on March 24, 1611, for the latter to identify it as genuinely his own work. The reason we know some of the content of the original letter is that this duplicate is preserved. The archbishop's inquiry "is of special interest as indicating the value of Clavius' testimony in favor of Galileo, for it seems to indicate that fears were entertained that possibly someone might have taken occasion of the reputation of Clavius to gain support for the new observations by forging letters of approval in his name."[35] At the end of the letter the Elector also observed that he had a telescope of his own, sent to him by Galileo himself, but that he was unable to see anything with it; for that reason in the same letter he asked Clavius to send him a good instrument like his own.[36]

On March 29, 1611, Galileo was finally at Rome. The following day he immediately visited the Roman College where he engaged in a long discussion with Clavius and two of his disciples, judged by Galileo as "the most understanding of the profession," Grienberger, already mentioned, and the Belgian Odon van Maelcote (1572–1615) who from 1606 taught mathematics at the Roman College. On April 1, that is, two days after the visit, Galileo hastened to write: "I have found that the fathers named, having finally recognized the truth of the new Medicean planets, have observed them continuously for two months, and continue to do so. We checked their observations against mine and found perfect agreement."[37] Three weeks later, April 22: "All the experts, especially the Jesuit fathers, agree with me, as everybody will soon know."[38]

Clavius' long friendship for Galileo, a friendship ending only with the death of the former on February 6, 1612, not to mention his confirmation of the Pisan astronomer's discoveries and of the Copernican interpretation which he had deduced from them,[39] had a definitive and perhaps even preponderant influence in gaining for Galileo's discoveries the almost universal acceptance of the learned world, even if the disappearance of the old professor and several of his abler disciples[40] rendered it incapable of preventing, on the part of Ecclesiastical Authority, the injunction of 1616 and the sentence of 1633.

7. The Link Connecting Galileo with China

At this point there is presented to us the link of connection between Galileo and China: it is the many-sided figure of a Swiss scientist,[41] who has already been a student of the great Tuscan at Padua in the faculty of medicine in 1603–1604. As an intimate friend of his teacher, he later was enthusiastic about the discoveries, and when he became a Jesuit and went to China as a missionary he retained this enthusiasm, striving to make the discoveries known in the Middle Kingdom. His name was John Schreck, but at least from 1603 on he Latinized this to Terrentius. We shall give him his original name.

Schreck was one of a few friends and scientists to whom Galileo showed the new planets at Cesi's Villa Malvasia above San Pancrazio on the Janiculum on April 14, 1611. A few days afterwards he had a similar experience in the gardens of the Tuscan ambassador at Rome, known today as the Villa Medici. This event evidently impressed him, as eleven years later, deep in China, he remembered somebody on the Trinità dei Monti who refused to look through Galileo's telescope for fear of being forced to believe something against his will.[42]

Prince Cesi, mentioned above, in 1603 founded the Academy of the Lincei [i.e. Lynxes, or "the sharp-sighted," a learned scientific society], which consisted only of five members in all until Galileo became the sixth, on April 25, 1611, during his second visit to Rome. The seventh academician, admitted eight days after Galileo (May 3), was our Schreck, who wrote in the still-extant register of the Academy: "Ego Johannes Terrentius, alias Schreck, Lyncaeus, Sebastiani filius, Costantiensis, aetatis anno XXXV, salutis, 1611, die Maij 3, Romae manu propria scripsi." ["I, John Terrentius, alias Schreck, Lincean, son of Sebastian, native of Constance, 35 years of age, wrote (this) by my own hand at Rome, May 3, in the Year of Salvation 1611."]

8. *The Solemn Convocation at the Roman College*

A few days after Galileo's arrival on his second visit to Rome, he was formally received at the Roman College. Clavius and the students of the new astronomy, the so-called "academicians of Father Clavius," organized a convocation in his honor. At least three cardinals were invited, and many princes, literati, and scholars of all kinds. Father Van Maelcote gave the introductory speech, presenting the guest as one of the most celebrated and fortunate astronomers of our age ("inter astronomos nostri temporis et celeberrimos et felicissimos merito numerandus"). He spoke of the *Sidereal Messenger*, in which Galileo the preceding year published some of his marvelous discoveries: the true face of the moon, the throng of stars and nebulae, and above all the four planets moving around Jupiter at various intervals and periods. The orator also spoke of the new *Messenger Sidereal*,[43] published later by the Roman College as confirmation of these discoveries by observations made at the college by the students of the new astronomy.[44] The convocation was a veritable triumph, as Galileo's friend Mark Welser recognized.

9. *Grienberger Defends Galileo Against a Jesuit*

The professors at the Roman College not only paid Galileo the tribute of public praise in this circumstance, but shortly afterwards they even defended him against an imprudent Jesuit writer. While Galileo was still at Rome, Grienberger received an essay on the subject: *The Height of the Lunar Mountains*,[45] an inquiry which later became known

.oblem of Mantua. The actual author of this essay was a forty-
.ld Jesuit, Darius Tamburelli (1570–1618), professor of math-
.ics at Parma.[46] I do not know why Grienberger supposed that
: author was Father Joseph Biancani, S. J., of the same college.
However that may be, the tract contained some disrespectful remarks
about Galileo. The professor of the Roman College examined the
document along with Galileo and, on the same day that the latter left
Rome, June 4, 1611, wrote to Biancani advising him to be more dis-
crete in talking about these matters. Polemicizing with his brother, at
a certain point he exclaimed: Let us admit even that there are not
mountains on the moon, or that Galileo has not taken the true diameter
of this planet. Is, then, this a reason for rejecting all the affirmations
of Galileo? "Sed esto, non sint. Numquid propterea nihil demonstrat
Galileus? O miserum Galileum, o infelicem qui verum Lunae diametrum
ad calculum non assumpserit!" ["But, granted that they (the mountains
on the moon) do not exist. Does Galileo therefore prove nothing? O
wretched Galileo, O unhappy one who did not subsume in his calculation the correct diameter of the moon!"] This letter of charitable
reproof ended with a fraternal exhortation: "May Your Reverence
not be offended at this admonition, and, if possible, may you speak of
Mr. Galileo as a mathematician in a proper manner. I appreciate that
not all of what he says is according to the faith; but, on the other hand,
certain things said by him are not so absurd that he does not deserve
to be excused rather than to be given a public rebuff."[47] Father Biancani
replied that he was not the author of the accusing essay. He was, he
admitted, the censor, and as such he had tried to persuade the author
to delete the disrespectful phrases about the Pisan astronomer, but
without effect. Grienberger forwarded this reply to Galileo, who
thereupon found an occasion for a very long letter.[48] Meanwhile, the
actual author of the essay wrote his apology on November 11, 1611,
and begged Grienberger to inform Galileo how much he was esteemed
and revered[49] in Parma—he was "never praised enough." In later years,
Grienberger always retained sentiments of sympathy for Galileo.[50]

10. Galileo Jokes About the Novice, Schreck

Galileo left Rome on June 4, 1611, satisfied with his new triumphs. A few months later (November 1) Schreck became a novice in the Society of Jesus in Rome.[51] This gladdened and saddened the Pisan astronomer at the same time. The news came to him in a letter of December 3 from Prince Cesi,[52] and in another letter of the fifteenth of the same month, from Faber.[53] That Schreck should have left the Academy of the Lincei so soon after joining it to become a Jesuit seems to have struck Galileo as droll, for he quipped (December 19): "The news of Mr. Terrentius has displeased me for the loss to our society as much as, on the other hand, it has pleased me for his holy resolution and for the gain to the other society, to which I owe so much."[54]

11. Scientific Letters from India to the Roman College

At about this time [1610 or 1611] two letters came to Clavius and Grienberger at Rome from a missionary in India, the Piedmontese Jesuit, Anthony Rubino (1578–1643), and they bore the dates October 25 and 28, 1609, respectively. The young missionary, barely thirty-one years of age, in his letter to Clavius thanked him for his *Practical Geometry*,[55] a complimentary copy of which he had received and read and reread with particular pleasure. He also gave some information about the Brahmans, who, he wrote, "are devoted to study of the movements and aspects of the planets and stars, particularly of twenty-seven by which they govern and rule." He tried to learn their secret of predicting "the hour and minute of eclipses of the sun and moon," but was unsuccessful because they shared this knowledge only with relatives and in secret. Then he told about his own scientific pursuits. "Two years ago I made in this Badaga language a *Description of the Whole World*, with explanatory notes about all the kingdoms, provinces, and principal cities on earth. The Indians were astonished at it." Like Ricci in Peking, he presented a world map to a local raja. While he wrote this letter, he was busy constructing a map of

Bisnaga or Vijayanagar, and explained that, to determine the distances between the cities, he used two or three eclipses of the moon calculated according to the meridian of Venice. In this work he depended upon the *Ephemerides* of the Paduan astronomer John Anthony Magini, but he added: "I always have some scruple, as I find that the *Ephemerides* of Magini very frequently err, not only by minutes, but by whole hours." He asked, accordingly, for other *Ephemerides*, "to make greater accuracy possible."[56] His later letter [that of October 28] to Grienberger said the same.[57]

These two letters left Chandrapur in India at the end of October or the beginning of November, 1609. They may have reached the Eternal City at the end of 1610, or more probably early in 1611, and thus were delivered at the time when the discoveries of Galileo were being given their full worth by him himself, and were being tested and confirmed, as we have seen, by the professors and pupils at the Roman College.

12. The Galilean Discoveries from the Roman College to India

Galileo's discoveries caused much excitement. But Clavius, who at best was slow in answering correspondents, was slower than ever, now that he was more than seventy years old, in replying to the missionary in India. Grienberger behaved similarly. But some one of the "academicians of Father Clavius" evidently knew of the young missionary-scientist's astronomical bent, for he hastened to send him information about Galileo's discoveries. We do not have this letter to Rubino, but we have a second letter in answer to it, from Rubino to Grienberger, which indicates sufficiently the tenor of the letter that left Italy for India probably in May or June 1611. This second letter of Father Rubino, dated November 2, 1612, lets us glimpse the enthusiasm excited in the young missionary-scientist by the sensational news of these discoveries. He not only asked for nothing more nor less than a telescope, but insisted that, if it were impossible to send one, a treatise be sent him on the question, if there were such a thing, or at the very least that the principles of its construction be indicated as clearly as possible so that he could make this instrument himself in India. How he multiplies his insistent expressions! To make certain that Father

Grienberger would respond he appealed to his charitable feelings. Then before closing the letter he returns again to the theme, describing how he imagined the telescope would look. In his own words: "Somebody wrote me from Italy that certain *occhiali* [eye-pieces] have been invented by means of which objects 15 or 20 miles away are seen clearly and many discoveries have been made in the heavens, particularly in the planets. Your Reverence will do me a great favor by sending me these, together with a little treatise on such *occhiali*, if there is a demonstration of the things one sees by them. But if Your Reverence does not have the occasion or the money to send me these, please send me *in writing and in figures*, as clearly as possible, the manner of their construction, so that I may have them made in this land of many officials and abundance of crystals. Please accept this small task for love of me, and may the occupation not weary you which gives me the utmost pleasure." It is quite obvious that the news interested him exceedingly, since he exhausts his vocabulary in begging the professor of the Roman College, with lively insistence, to send him something appropriate. The letter ends with this postscript: "The *occhiali*, I imagine, are made in the manner of pyramids, wide at the beginning and sharp at the end, and at the beginning perhaps they are rather concave; *et si ita est vivant in eternum Perspectivi, qui visionem fieri per extramissionem deffendunt*[58] [and if this is so, long live the Masters of Perspective who maintain that the visual image is made by emission]. Your Reverence, please help me in everything, and send me everything written and well explained."[59]

13. *The First Chinese Text on the Galilean Discoveries* (1615)

We do not know whether or in what manner Rubino's request was satisfied. But we may be certain that he immediately informed the missionaries in China, because in this same letter of November 2 he confessed: "Perhaps I shall go to China. The calls from thence are insistent." The reason, of course, was his scientific preparations and interest. Thus, from India the news of the telescope and of the astronomical discoveries made by means of it spread quickly to China, where in 1615 Father Emmanuel Diaz [the Younger] S.J., printed a small book in Chinese on *Problems of Astronomy* or *The Sphere*.[60] After describing such astronomical phenomena as eclipses, the light of the sun and moon, long and short days, and so forth, he added a last page (f. 43*a–b*) of description of the telescope and its discoveries, indicating that the news reached him only shortly before publication.

"Most of what has been explained hitherto is based upon observations made by the naked eye. But the vision of the naked eye is short. How can it measure the least part of the exceedingly small and admirable points of the firmament? Lately a famous Western scientist versed in astronomy[61] has undertaken to observe the mysteries of the sun, moon, and stars. But grieved at the weakness of his eyes, he constructed a marvelous instrument to aid them. With this instrument an object of the size of 1 *ch'ih* 尺,[62] placed at a distance of 60 *li* 里,[63] seems to be right in front of the eyes. Viewed with this instrument, the moon appears a thousand times larger. Venus with this instrument looks as big as the moon. Its light increases or decreases in the same manner as that of the disk of the moon. Saturn with this instrument resembles the figure here annexed,[64] round like a hen's egg, with two small stars on

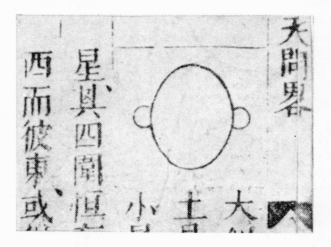

Fig. 1. The figure of "three-bodied" Saturn, from the first Chinese text on Galileo's discoveries, *The Sphere* (f. 43*a–b*), by E. Diaz the Younger, S.J. (1615).

its sides. But whether they adhere to it is not exactly known.[65] This instrument shows Jupiter always to be attended by four small stars moving around it very rapidly; some of them are on its east; some on its west; or {vice versa} some on its west, some on its east. Or all may be on its east, or all on its west. Their motion, however, is quite different from that {of the stars}[66] of the 28 constellations; because while the stars remain {in the orbit} of the seven planets, these are stars of a special class. The heaven of the constellations with this instrument reveals a great quantity of small stars, close together, the light of which is collected as if it formed a white chain; it is what now one calls the Milky Way." His book closes with the hope: "The day that this instrument arrives in China we shall give more details of its admirable use."

14. *Rapidity of the Diffusion of this News*

In the second decade of the seventeenth century we are not, of course, in the age of the steamboat or telegraph, still less of the radio. Whoever wished to go to the Middle or Far East had first of all to be Portuguese either by birth or by a certain legal fiction which one acquired by leaving Lisbon, sole port of embarcation for Portuguese Asia. But ships, when they left Lisbon at all, left only once a year, in March; and, after rounding the Cape of Good Hope, they arrived at Goa, if they arrived at all, only after six months of terrible crossing; thus, if all went well, in September of the same year. Then in India the traveler had to halt at least until April of the following year when the monsoons would permit another ship to sail for the port of Macao, where it arrived towards the end of July. In short, it was necessary to count on two or three years for a voyage from Rome to Macao, if all went well.[67] What was true for travelers was also true for letters. These to cover the distance from Rome to Peking, or vice versa, easily required three, four, five, seven years. A letter from Valignano, still preserved, was written at Macao on October 10, 1589, and did not reach Rome until 1606, as a diligent and intelligent archivist noted, that is, not until after seventeen years! In a similar age the news of Galileo's discoveries crossed the seas and made the immense passage from Italy to the Chinese hinterland in a brief interval, 1610 to 1614 or 1615. The great scientist could not have wished for a more rapid spread of his discoveries! The Jesuit missionaries in this deserved well of science, and, if he could have known of it, also of the great scientist.

15. *Again, Send Us Astronomers!*

Up to this point only the news of Galileo's discoveries reached China. From now on we shall take into account scientists who also went there, who knew and admired Galileo, who were his intimate friends, and who, at any rate before 1616, were almost as convinced Copernicans as he.

Let us remember Ricci's insistences on having missionary-astronomers who could correct the mistaken Chinese calendar.[68] He died in May 1610 without having received the astronomers so much desired and awaited. Julius Aleni in 1630 wrote in Chinese and printed the *Life of Mr. Matthew Ricci of the Great Occident*,[69] of which the Vatican Library (Borgia Cin. 350³) preserves a very rare copy. . . . Towards the end of this *Life*, Aleni expressed himself thus: "Before Dr. Ricci died he saw an occasion to preach religion in the fact that the calendar of the reigning dynasty had been mistaken for many years. The Ministry of Rites 禮部 in a memorial to the throne {on this topic} proposed to entrust its correction to Dr. Ricci and to Dr. Pantoja. The imperial rescript was favorable. However, Dr. Ricci, conscious that he could not alone bear the weight of religious propaganda and such a grave state office, wrote to his country requesting one or two confrères who would bring many European books to be translated. Thus, I, Julius, and two or three others of my brothers, like Dr. Francis Sambiasi and Dr. Peter Van Spiere,[70] have come from afar via the sea. But Dr. Ricci died in this same year of our arrival" (B, f. 20a). Thus we come to know that these three missionaries, who, however, were still not true astronomers, were sent to China precisely in reply to the reiterated demands of Ricci of his superiors in Rome.

After the error of a half hour made by the imperial astronomers for the eclipse of December 15, 1610, the director of the Astronomical Bureau, Chou Tzŭ-yü 周子愚,[71] boldly proposed in 1611 to avail himself of the services of two other Jesuits: Nicholas Longobardo[72] and Sabatino De Ursis.[73] They were to be assisted by Dr. Paul Hsü Kuang-ch'i 徐光啓[74] and Dr. Leo Li Chih-tsao 李之藻[75] in the translation of scientific books which the European missionaries brought with them. This memorial remained unanswered because conservative old mandarins opposed it. But two years later Li Chih-tsao was summoned to the capital to prepare for the above-mentioned correction, and he renewed the attack with a more urgent petition, requesting that Pantoja, Longobardo, De Ursis, and Diaz the Younger be put in charge of translating European books.

After Ricci's death, De Ursis, on September 2, 1610, wrote to the Assistant to the General in Charge of the Portuguese Province and Missions at Rome, Father Anthony Mascarenas, insisting upon having some mathematicians and mathematical books. He wrote: "When I first came to this mission, Father Matthew Ricci called me to this house at Peking. He wanted me to do mathematical work because he knew that I had some acquaintance with mathematics. He kept me at this for the three years {1607–1610} during which I was with him. But since we have no books we can do nothing. The only books we have are Father Clavius' *Gnomica*, *Sphere*, and *Astrolabe*. The truth is, as Ricci said, that we must work with both hands, the right in the affairs of God, the left in these affairs. We cannot do less, and what has been accomplished hitherto has been done by this method. So I propose to Your Reverence that you send us a father who understands mathematics thoroughly, particularly astrology {=astronomy}, together with some books on this subject. I shall take care to conform to the instructions my superiors send me, and to the purposes of Father Ricci whose abundant experience at this station enabled him to cast much light." At the close of this letter he added: "Remember me to everybody and ask Father Christopher Grienberger for some beautiful and curious mathematical literature to please these Chinese literati. It will be of great service to the Lord, as I have previously written."[76] From this it appears that De Ursis, like Rubino, was in correspondence with Grienberger, Clavius' successor in the chair of mathematics at the Roman College.

With still greater authority than that of De Ursis, the Sicilian Longobardo, successor to Ricci as superior of the mission, on November 23, 1610, wrote to the General in person: "If Your Paternity wishes to know the most proper and effective way to promote this mission, then in everybody's judgment it is to send us many and good subjects, as has been written other times, and particularly some able mathematicians," with many books.[77] Longobardo wrote again, October 15, 1612, to the General of the Order, insisting even more emphatically upon having mathematical books and instruments and a pair of distinguished scientists. I translate from his Portuguese text: "For us it is certain that mathematics will open the field at which we are aiming. For this we need mathematical books and instruments, this particularly so now that after the petitions of the mathematicians of Peking the translation of these books into Chinese is being considered. Also a pair of noted mathematicians is necessary, so that we may avoid falling into errors that would discredit us. Know, moreover, that our plan, and the plan of Dr. Paul Hsü Kuang-ch'i, is to effect translations of philosophy and theology for the king under the shadow of mathematics. Indeed, we have already deftly done this in a memorial to the throne treating of mathematics. If this plan is successful, two or three missionaries will professedly occupy themselves with these scientific studies, at Peking, while the rest of the missionaries will calmly and safely attend the Christians in other parts of the kingdom. Those who are in charge of the translation will live on a salary paid by the king. In order to get the best possible results from mathematics, it would be advisable to tell the fathers of the other residencies to learn enough mathematics to be able to illustrate in some way the books [of mathematics] that are printed. See to it, also, that the fathers who are to enter the hinterland have a course in mathematics, as was the case this year."[78]

Still begging for scientific aid, John Rodriguez, known as The Interpreter or *Tsu-ji* (old romanization *Tsu-zu* 通事),[79] wrote to the General from Canton on January 25, 1612, the following passage which I translate from the Portuguese: "Not only the fathers in the interior of China, but we also in Macao beg to petition Your Paternity to send to this mission without delay some fathers well versed in mathematics, so that we shall make no mistakes in these matters, which God forbid! The missionaries already here are not versed in mathematics, although what little they know is more solid than what the Chinese know. Accordingly, the fathers have decided to proceed slowly until Your Paternity thinks it well to send a good quantity of mathematical books of every kind for their own use as well as for translation. The fathers have resolved to give a public course in mathematics at the court of Peking, of which Father Aleni will be in charge very soon. At present he is about to enter the hinterland according to news thence. I speak so much of this matter because it was written to me from Macao that if an occasion presented itself I should inform Your Paternity so that you can come to our aid with solicitude."[80]

Towards the end of 1612, Father Nicholas Longobardo decided to send a young Belgian missionary, Nicholas Trigault,[81] to Rome to present the needs of the mission before the General and the Pope. Among other duties he was to obtain a great scientific library as a gift from the Pope and the Catholic princes, as well as two of the most illustrious mathematicians in the Society at that time, from the General of the Order, to occupy themselves with astronomy at the court of the Son of Heaven in China.

Trigault reached the Eternal City in November or December 1614. He went to work immediately. His request for missionary-astronomers was favorably received by the Order, since several Jesuits, some already celebrated, others giving promise of becoming so, volunteered to go to China.

16. *Astronomers Volunteer to Go to China*

Among others, three illustrious scientists volunteered to go to China. They were Gregory of St. Vincent, Christopher Scheiner, and John Baptist Cysat.

Gregory of St. Vincent (1584–1667), a former student at the Roman College, was a great favorite of his teachers Clavius and Grienberger for his rare mathematical ability. His name is still known in the history of geometry, and particularly in conic sections and infinitesimal calculus. He attended the convocation in Galileo's honor at the Roman College in 1611, and perhaps took active part.[82] Almost fifty years later he recalled this impressive event with pleasure, as well as the hundreds of nights he spent with Clavius making telescopic observations. He remembered observing Jupiter's satellites, the mountains on the moon, and the phases of Venus. The last phenomena, as was noted at the convocation, demonstrated clearly that in spite of the philosophers Venus moves around the sun: "Et Venerem circa solem verti manifeste demonstravimus non absque Philosophorum murmure."[83] ["And we demonstrated clearly that Venus turns around the sun in spite of the growls of the philosophers."]

Christopher Scheiner (1575–1650) was a professor of mathematics at the University of Ingolstadt. His name is associated with the invention of the pantograph. He observed the sunspots in March 1611, perhaps independently of Galileo, but after him. Unfortunately this coincidence led to controversy between him and the great Pisan scientist.[84]

John Cysat (1588–1657), a Swiss, was one of Scheiner's abler pupils, who subsequently became a professor of mathematics at Ingolstadt. His name is connected with the discovery of the nebula of Orion.

Gregory of St. Vincent volunteered on December 18, 1615, to follow Trigault. The latter, he wrote, "seeks companions, chiefly mathematicians." The General granted permission on February 16 of the following year, pointing out that Gregory was preferred above many others. Gregory, however, possibly let himself be influenced by his brothers and his rector, the mathematician d'Aguillon (1566–1617), none of whom wanted to see the young man's promising scientific career cut off. At any rate, he renounced his privilege in favor of another candidate, and did not sail for China.[85]

Christopher Scheiner's failure to go to China was because General Vitelleschi refused permission. The General judged that it would be more to the common good for Scheiner to remain in Europe and train missionary-scientists. The General wrote to him on July 15, 1617: "Your Reverence in your letter has explained your inclination towards the mission in China. I have weighed the reasons put forward by Your Reverence, *pro* and *contra*, in regard to this question. Finally, I have decided that for the greater glory of God and for the good of the Society it is preferable for Your Reverence to stay in Europe, and energetically promote mathematical studies. Thus, you will be able to do by means of your disciples in China what you will not be able to do yourself."[86] Galileo without knowing it almost had one enemy the less in Europe!

John [Baptist] Cysat also volunteered for the mission in China and was accepted. His provincial, Father Melchior Hartel, however, instantly wrote to Rome raising the objection that professors of mathematics were needed in the province at home. The General admitted the truth of this argument, and, in June 1617, the already granted permission was revoked.[87]

17. *Mathematicians and Astronomers Off for China*

So none of these three embarked for China. But those who did go were not inferior to them.

Among the twenty-two missionaries who set sail with Trigault from Lisbon on April 16, 1618, were several mathematicians: the Italian James Rho, the Bohemian Wenceslaus Pantaleon Kirwitzer,[88] the Austrian John Alberich, the Swiss John Schreck, whom we have already met, and the German John Adam Schall von Bell, who was destined to become famous in the history of Chinese science.

The crossing was, as always, extremely difficult. Of 636 passengers, packed in the boat as tight as sardines, a good 330, that is, more than half, fell ill during the voyage. The mortality, however, was comparatively low. According to the passengers, as many as 200 were expected to die, but the fact is that only 45 died, of whom 5 were missionaries. One of them was John Alberich, formerly professor of sciences at the University of Ingolstadt.[89]

18. *Kirwitzer a Convinced Copernican*

Wenceslaus Kirwitzer must have been extraordinarily intelligent, and might have acquired a fairly good name in the history of science if death had not snatched him prematurely from his studies. Two unpublished letters of his from Graz, addressed to Grienberger, are preserved. In the first one, which carries the date December 26, 1614, he openly recognized Ptolemy's errors: "vidi Ptolomaeum et Alphonsum

Regem in suis tabulis astronomicis procul a veritate aberrare." ["I saw
that Ptolemy and King Alphonso in their astronomical tables wander
far from the truth."] Evidently he applied himself with ardor to the
observations of Copernicus and the study of the Prutenic tables. But
he was convinced that these, too, were not free from error, which led
him to lose some of his respect for the Polish astronomer. "Vidi
sextantem Copernici, quo ille plerosque caelestes motus observarat
multis in rebus non exactum, ut proinde non immerito parum apud
me authoritas Copernici maxime in Prutenicarum tabularum ceciderit."
["I saw that one of the six (books) of Copernicus,[90] in which were most
of his observations of the celestial motions, contained many inaccuracies,
so that accordingly not without reason his authority was diminished for
me a little, mostly in respect of the Prutenic tables."] Then he expressed
with great frankness his opinion of the geocentric and heliocentric
astronomical systems. The former without any reservation whatever
he called "false." "Communes illae {hypotheses} quae terram in centro
universi collocant, quas Maginus illustravit, falsae sunt." ["Those common (hypotheses) which place the earth in the center of the universe,
illustrated by Magini, are false."] But he did not thereby admit immediately the Copernican system. He believed the latter also false, but
he felt attracted toward it. "Copernici hypothesis quae terram mobilem
circumfert difficilis creditu est, quamvis phaenomena servet exactis-
sime."[91] ["The hypothesis of Copernicus, which carries the mobile
earth around in a circle, is difficult to believe, however exactly it may
save the phenomena."]

    We do not have Grienberger's answer to this first letter of Kirwitzer.
But if we may judge from the Bohemian astronomer's second letter
[June 7, 1615] to the professor at the Roman College, written after
receiving the reply to the first letter, we must conclude that Grienberger
declared himself clearly in favor of Copernicus, hence of Galileo. In
Kirwitzer's second letter, in fact, all hesitation is gone; he is a convinced Copernican. Better yet, contrary to a current opinion which
would make all Jesuits think alike, he was willing to grapple with
Scheiner in defense of Copernicus, and therefore of Galileo, whom,
however, he does not name. Scheiner's little book was recommended
for Kirwitzer's study by Grienberger. Kirwitzer, therefore, hastened to

read it, and to procure the theses of the same author.[92] Now that he had studied Scheiner's thought, he was replying to Grienberger as one who was acquainted with the cause. In his judgment, Scheiner was merely a destroyer who tore down all the hypotheses of others without putting anything in their place. "Multa ille contra hypotheses aliorum disputat, nullas proprias statuit." ["He argues much against the hypotheses of others, establishes none of his own."] Coming then to the focal point of the controversy, the Copernican system, he declared himself unambiguously: Father Scheiner thought he had crushed Copernicus with the weight of his arguments; nevertheless, the Copernican hypothesis is, in spite of his blows, more firm than ever. "Copernicum obruisse argumentis videtur, cuius tamen hypothesis inter reliquas adhuc est firmissima. Expediam, ut spero, nodos illos omnes, ostendamque difficultates illas nullum locum habere in Copernici hypothesi; quod ubi perfecero, per Patres professos nostros Roman proficiscentes, Reverentiae Vestrae tamquam Mathematicarum rerum Patroni transmittam."[93] ["I hope to untie all those knots (Scheiner's difficulties), and to show that those difficulties have no place in the hypothesis of Copernicus. When I finish this work I shall send it by means of our professed fathers going to Rome, to Your Reverence (for your inspection) as defender of mathematics."][94] This second letter, dated June 7, 1615, was written exactly eight months before the inhibitory decree of the Holy Office.

There is no reason to believe that this promise was not kept. In such case Kirwitzer's promised anti-Scheiner, pro-Copernicus essay could have reached the hands of Grienberger by the end of October or the beginning of November 1615, barely three months before the famous injunction, since the fathers who were to carry it were certainly in Rome on November 15, the day of the election of the new General of the Order, Mutius Vitelleschi. This proves how convinced a Copernican this Bohemian scientist was, destined for China. Unfortunately, however, notwithstanding my researches, I have not been able to trace this precious writing of Kirwitzer. That also he was a warm admirer of Galileo shines through from the following passage in this same letter: "Galilei modum minuta secunda horaria observandi, mirum quantum desiderem; Reverentia Vestra uti eum ubi eum re-

sciverit, mei etiam memor sit." ["I should like Galilei's amazing method
of observing by the second the hourly motions (of the heavenly bodies).
Please remember me to him, wherever Your Reverence knows he may
be."] On the other hand, he who might have been one of the first
and most convinced supporters of the new science in the Middle
Kingdom died prematurely in 1626, a few years after his arrival in
China, when the great work of the correction of the calender had not
yet even begun.

19. *Schreck's Insistent and Repeated Appeals to Galileo*

John Schreck, or Terrentius, mentioned above,[95] shortly after his
assignment to the Chinese mission, traveled through Europe in search
of books for the projected scientific library at Peking. When he visited
Milan he even asked Cardinal Frederick Borromeo for a telescope to
take with him to China. The Cardinal, not knowing where to find
Schreck, sent an instrument on March 30, 1616, to Faber at Rome,
with the request: "Deliver it to him safely;" and his letter closes with
the words: "Please give it to the father at your earliest opportunity."[96]
If, as is most probable, Schreck took this telescope with him, it would
be the first one to arrive in China. The young scientist at the same
time busied himself with the projected reform of the Chinese calendar.
In this connection he frequently asked help from Galileo, whose assistance he considered of the utmost importance to the missionary-
scientists at Peking. Two months after the injunction of the Holy
Office he wrote from Milan to his friend, the young German, John
Faber, at Rome, April 6, 1616, how displeased he was with the injunction imposed on Galileo. He feared that it would prevent the Pisan
scientist from sending him the eclipse calculations he needed for his
work in China. "Certainly," he wrote, "the edict has come as a great
inconvenience to me. Now I shall not expect the calculation of eclipses
which I requested from him in the interests of the Chinese." He did
not, however, lose all hope, but begged Prince Cesi to attempt to get
the computations for him from Galileo. In evident allusion to the
injunction he promised to observe complete silence. Also he was anxious
to learn whether Galileo's calculations differed from Tycho Brahe's.[97]

Since nothing came from Florence, there were always new pleas from Milan. A month and a half later, in a second letter to Faber, Schreck wrote: "I only desire from Mr. Galileo his method of calculating eclipses of the sun and moon, that is, his solar and lunar hypotheses, before I leave for China, because he will have made, no doubt, a little calculation much more exact than that of Tycho Brahe. Let him inform Prince Cesi whether there is any hope of my having this calculation, or whether he will be willing under certain conditions to communicate the calculation to me before my departure, for the public good of the Chinese mission. Or, at the very least, whether he will give me information about one eclipse or another during this coming year so that I may take account of the difference between Galileo's calculation and that of Tycho Brahe and our Ruderauf."[98]

He waited in vain another month, then wrote again to Faber, June 14, 1616: ["Greet Prince Cesi most courteously . . .] through whom, at his convenience, before I leave Europe, I earnestly hope to obtain something from Galileo useful to our Chinese in calculating eclipses."[99] Meanwhile about four months later, September 3, Faber announced to Galileo that he should send his observations of Saturn to "Cardinal Borromeo, who is most curious about these novelties. I am under obligation to him on account of Father Terrentius, who at present is with Father Nicholas {Trigault} at Augsburg."[100]

All these requests from the Swiss missionary for Galileo's scientific contribution in the work of reforming the Chinese calendar were pressing indeed. That he continued to demand and hope in spite of everything proves his high esteem of the Pisan mathematician.

Schreck spent about three years, 1615–1618, in preparing for his departure for China. During this time he used his science and his personal connections with the learned world to collect everything in various European countries that would be serviceable to him in the scientific labor he anticipated in China. He solicited gifts on all sides, from great princes of the time and from patrons of the arts, as well as from academicians and noted scientists. Among those he approached were, for example, Fabius Colonna, Nicholas Anthony Stelliola, John Quietan Ruderauf (Latinized Remus) a German mathematician and physician, Marino Ghetaldi of Ragusa, a distinguished mathematician,

Prince Cesi himself, and, in particular, Galileo. Fifteen days before his embarcation for the Middle Kingdom, whence he would never return, he wrote from Lisbon on March 31, 1618: "Si quid novi prodeat a Domino Columna, Valerio, Remo, Ghetaldo, Galileo, et similibus curiosis, quaeso, me faciat participem; ero vicissim non ingratus."[101] ["If anything new comes forth from Mr. Colonna, Valerius, Remus, Ghetaldi, Galileo, or similar inquisitive persons, I beg you to make me a sharer. I shall be grateful."] All of these, in other words, were asked to contribute from their scientific publications to the forming of the projected library at Peking. If we count the approximately five hundred books already given by the Pope in 1616,[102] books given by princes, scholars, and authors, and books acquired in other ways, it is probable that the missionaries took with them more than seven thousand volumes.[103] In those days seven thousand volumes represented scientific wealth not within everybody's reach.

20. Insistences Continue from China

The missionaries left Lisbon on April 16, 1618, and reached Macao in July of the following year. Two years later Schreck, from Hangchow, capital of Chekiang Province, resumed his insistences with the same friend, Faber, to have from Galileo the scientific contributions always awaited by him for the reform of the calendar. "Mr. Galileo de' Galilei could do nothing more appreciated or acceptable to the mission of China than to send his theory of the sun and moon without the tables, since the Chinese eagerly expect of us that we give them a calculation of eclipses more exact than what they have. Tycho has something good, but at times he errs by a quarter of an hour. If what I ask could be had through the intercession of Prince Cesi, he would become with you and Galileo the third benefactor of the mission of China."[104]

A year afterward, on April 22, 1622, he renewed the attack, writing always to the same friend, Faber, from a city of the present-day province of Kiangsu, called Kiating: "As I have written another time, I have a very great desire—*summopere exoptarem*—to receive from Galileo his calculation of eclipses, especially solar, according to his recent observations; this is for us supremely necessary for the correction of the calendar. If we have not been thrown out of the country, we owe it uniquely to this correction. Prince Cesi without doubt can intercede for us with Galileo to send us this calculation."

Seeing, however, that all his requests had remained fruitless for a good six years, he thought he would have recourse to the highest intercessors, not only Prince Cesi, as always, but even the Archduchess of Tuscany, who might be made interested in the matter either by Archduke Leopold or by the emperor himself. He added, in fact: "Prince Cesi without doubt can obtain this calculation from Galileo. Perhaps the Archduchess of Florence herself can obtain it if she is asked by her brother the emperor, or by Archduke Leopold. But I fear that all these people are preoccupied by an entirely different matter, and that it is inopportune to attract their attention to a matter of such little importance {for them}." Six years had passed since the famous injunction of the Holy Office which prohibited the Pisan scientist from sustaining in public or in private the Copernican doctrine of the motion of the earth. Therefore, Schreck turned to promising the most absolute silence. And, as he had been able also to know something about the contest between Galileo and one of his brothers in Europe, Scheiner, over priority in the discovery of sunspots, he promised to give Galileo the honor belonging to him whenever he wanted to accede to his request, so many times reiterated: "I promise silence and the honor due the author. In fact, in this class of things I do not wish to arrogate anything to myself, and I very willingly praise the activity of others in whatever branch of knowledge."[105]

21. *Dry and Decisive Negative Reply of Galileo*

All the attempts of Schreck to make himself heard by Galileo were in vain. Not content with the personal friendship which bound him to his brother member of the Academy of the Lincei, Schreck had moved all the pawns to succeed in his intent. He had made use of his greatest friend in Rome, John Faber, who was also an intimate friend of the Pisan scientist. Faber, in his turn, to please the missionary-scientist, had worked on Galileo by means of two other Linceans, Virginius Cesarini[106] and Prince Frederick Cesi, exceedingly close friends of the great astronomer; he had also made use of Galileo's favorite disciple, Marius Guiducci,[107] without obtaining better result; finally he had worked personally and directly on the celebrated scientist. All was in vain. After eight years of continuous and always more pressing and authoritative insistences—remaining unfortunately useless —on May 10, 1624, Galileo finished by saying that he had nothing to send to China. He was then for the fourth time at Rome, guest of Prince Cesi. The day after the useless effort, Faber wrote to Cesi: "I was yesterday evening with our Mr. Galilei, who lives near the Madalena. . . . He has not communicated to me any of his business, but I am at his command, and I shall see him often. . . . I have also talked with him concerning the observations of solar eclipses for Terrentius, but he tells me that he has nothing."[108]

In the judgment of the diligent editor of the Lincean correspondence, the lamented Professor Joseph Gabrieli, to whose erudite publications I owe the above-cited texts on Shreck, this negative reply of the great Lincean was "rather dry, quick, and apparently untrue."[109] The personal dispute existing between Galileo on the one side and two Jesuits, Horace Grassi of the Roman College, [with whom he debated] on comets from 1618 on, and Christopher Scheiner of Ingolstadt, [with whom he argued] on sunspots from 1611,[110] had perhaps become, insensibly for the Tuscan astronomer, a direct tension between him and the Jesuits. This would tend to explain his dry and annoyed answer. The matter is to be deplored, among many other reasons, for [its effect on] the history of the introduction of the sciences into China at the beginning of the seventeenth century.

22. *After Galileo the Missionaries Turn to Kepler*

Discouraged, at last, in getting help from Galileo, Schreck wrote to his colleagues at Ingolstadt in 1623 to send him something useful for the prediction of eclipses. He begged also for new books, such as Kepler's *Hipparchus*, or "something else by Galileo."[111] This indirect appeal was Schreck's last call upon the Italian astronomer. The Jesuit Father Albert Curtz (1600–1671), a great friend of Kepler, forwarded the letter to the German scientist, who must have received it in about the middle of November 1627—four years after it was originally sent. Kepler, in contrast to Galileo, replied immediately and in detail to all Schreck's questions. His long Latin letter (December 1627) is still preserved. Its closing sentence is a good wish for the conversion of the Chinese, expressed in a very Christian formula: "Quod ratum esse velit Is cui Pater aeternus gentes in haereditatem dedit, Christus Iesus, Deus et homo, Dominusque noster. Amen."[112] ["May Jesus Christ, God and man, and our Lord, to Whom the Eternal Father gave the heathen as an inheritance, will that it (the conversion of the Chinese) be fulfilled. Amen."][113] Kepler sent to China, also, in answering, two parts (*quaderni*) of the Rudolphine tables, which were just then being printed.[114] A copy of the *Supplementum Ephemeridum Magini*, printed at Venice in 1614 and still preserved in the former library of the Jesuits at Peking, has on its margins many handwritten references to the works of Kepler, proof that these works were put to immediate use by the missionaries at Peking.[115] Doubtless the only reason that Kepler played this role in the scientific enterprise of the reformation of the Chinese calendar was Galileo's refusal to respond to the often expressed desire of the missionaries in China for his scientific contribution.

The missionary-scientists, however, never lost interest in the great Italian astronomer. We have indisputable proof of this in their efforts to bring the telescope and its discoveries to the attention of the Chinese.

John Adam Schall von Bell, who won fame among the Chinese as an astronomer during about thirty years, and who was present at the convocation in Galileo's honor at the Roman College in May 1611, did not forget him when on July 15, 1619, he landed at Macao. Still less did he forget him when along with Schreck he reached Peking on January 25, 1623.

23. *The First Chinese Treatise on the Telescope* (1626)

Three years later, in fact, between September 20 and October 19, 1626, Schall signed the preface of a little treatise on the telescope, which could have appeared in print before the end of that same year. This was the first time that educated Chinese had a complete description of the marvelous Galilean instrument and its construction. The treatise was dictated by Schall and put in Chinese by a Christian Chinese, of whom in the present case we know the name, a certain John Li Tsu-pai 李祖白.[116] The work contained two sheets of preface and seventeen of text, that is to say, in all, according to the European count, thirty-eight pages. Although it is not a translation of the *Telescope*[117] by Jerome Sirturi, published at Frankfort in 1618, as has been ascertained by me by comparing the two publications, nevertheless that [book] of Schall must have taken its clue precisely from this.

In the preface the author makes a eulogy on the eye and the ear, preferring the first to the second. Aristotle, he says, said that from the ear science is born, because that which enters by means of hearing penetrates most clearly to the intelligence. Plato said, however, that the eye is the master of philosophy, because it guides from matter to spirit, from the visible to the invisible, conducting to the threshold of philosophy. It is the eye which distinguishes number, magnitude, and distance of objects. Thus, all that augments the visual potency ought to be held in great esteem. In such a manner the author introduces the theme of the telescope.

In the beginning of the treatise, Father Schall asks this question: "Who invented the telescope?" And he replies: "An occidental astronomer invented it." Galileo is not named either here or in following texts, unless in 1640, without doubt for the simple reason that for the Chinese of that time a European name, phoneticized in Chinese, something like *Chia-li-lê-io*, would have signified little or nothing more than a barbarian name. Let one think of the reverse case of the name of a Chinese scientist in an occidental treatise on astronomy.

Immediately next are enumerated the advantages of the telescope, which are called "immense." "It is easy for all," it is said, "to see near and great objects, but it is difficult to see those which are little and distant. Now with the telescope there is no longer either small object or distant object. In short, with the telescope both heaven and earth become part of our visual field. In the mountains or on the sea, with this, one can see ahead of time incursions of brigands or pirates. It is besides of great use to everybody. It is truly an instrument which unexpectedly renders sight acute, and it is the joy of the scientist."

There come now scientific applications made possible by the telescope. For this the Galilean discoveries are passed in review.

"In the moon," it is said, "one sees illuminated parts and obscure parts; the first are convex, the others concave; in other words, one is dealing here with mountains and valleys of the moon. If with one eye one observes the moon without the telescope, and with the other with the telescope, the difference is extraordinarily great.

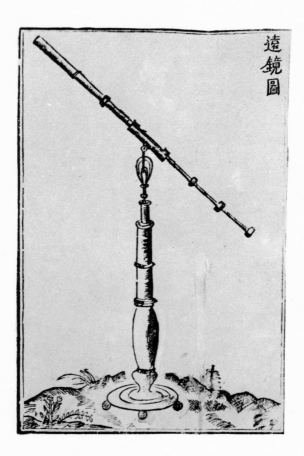

Fig. 2. The telescope. From *The Telescope*, by J. A. Schall.

"Venus in a year has phases and quarters which resemble the phases and quarters which the moon has in a month. It is not always equally visible, because it travels around the sun; when it is above the sun, its light is visible, when on the other hand it is below the sun, its light is invisible. Its size appears more or less great according to the position which it occupies with respect to the sun, according, that is to say, whether it is above, below, to the right, or to the left of the sun.

"The sun at rising and setting is not perfectly round, but has the appearance of a hen's egg. The reason is to be found in the fine dust which rises in the air. Between 5 and 7 A.M. and between 5 and 7 P.M. the sun looks toothed like a saw. It has spots which vary in number, size, and visibility, and which follow one another without fixed periodicity. They disappear entirely after fourteen days. Their cause is unknown.

"Jupiter has four stars moving around it according to fixed laws and epochs. Since they are also subject to eclipse this proves that they are not stars of the constellations. To know the distance between these and Jupiter we must know their orbit.

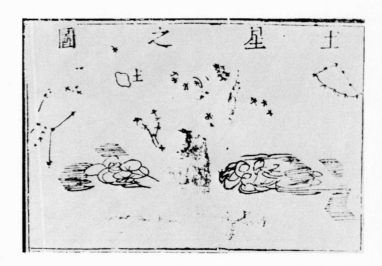

Fig. 3. Saturn. From *The Telescope*, by J. A. Schall.

"On either side of Saturn is a small star, both of which, after a long time, approach it and finally become one with it, having the appearance of the two ends of an egg or of two ears.

"Not only is the number of stars in the constellations tens of times greater than the number visible to the naked eye, but each of these stars is seen distinctly. For example, the stars of the Pleiades are not just seven but are more than thirty. The stars of the nebula, in Cancer, [Praesepe] the northern star of Orion,[118] and the small stars of the Milky Way, are distinguished with difficulty by the naked eye, but with this instrument are seen clearly. Thus also two stars of the Scorpion and two of the Great Bear, which the eye distinguishes with difficulty, with the telescope, on the other hand, appear quite far apart. The distances of the stars, calculated with this instrument, are exceedingly exact."

All these explanations are accompanied by illustrations to make the text more intelligible. Thus, at the beginning one sees a picture of a magnificent telescope pointed at the sky (Fig. 2). Then come the celestial revelations made by the telescope: two figures of the first and second quarters of the moon with dentated shadows, then other figures of Saturn (Fig. 3), the phases of Venus, the Great Bear, the sun rising

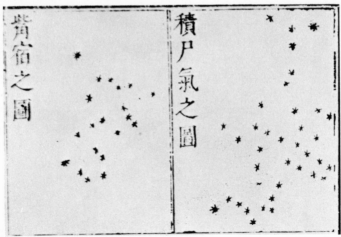

Fig. 4. Orion (on the left) and Praesepe (on the right). From *The Telescope*, by J. A. Schall.

and setting and with spots, the Milky Way, Jupiter's four satellites with their orbits, the nebula in Orion (Fig. 4), and so forth. The[119] rest of the work is devoted to lenses and the construction of the telescope.

In the following year, 1627, Dr. Philip Wang Chêng 王徵, in publishing his work, *Illustrated Explanation of the Instruments of Mechanics of the Far West*,[120] refers to Schall's *Treatise on the Telescope* and describes the instrument in these words: "First it is necessary to manufacture with glass some lenses which seem flat but which in fact are not so. At the mouth of the tube one puts that [lens] which one calls lens of the mouth of the tube, or concave lens, or front lens. Then at the back part of the tube one puts the lens [which is] a bit convex, called also eye-piece, or lens convex in the middle, or rear lens. If the proportion of the distances between the two lenses corresponds, one can see things. The lenses are only at the two extremities, but the tube can be elongated at will, being inserted in itself, and is capable of being lengthened or shortened. That one is preferable which is, by screw, capable of being raised or lowered and of being screwed or unscrewed to the right or left. But in looking one makes use of one eye only, going from objects which are on the far side of 60 paces up to 60 *li*. One can thus observe the moon, Venus, the sun, Jupiter, Saturn, and even the stars of the constellations. When one observes the sun or Venus one adds thereto a blue lens, or in observing the sun one places under the telescope a piece of white paper. Besides this, this instrument can be useful in sea voyages or for painting in a *camera obscura* or again in war." And explaining this last point he thus continues: "If there should break out unexpectedly a military revolution, whether by day or by night, making use in the latter case of the light produced by another, one can look at, from a distance, the place of the enemy, the encampments, the men, the horses, whether [the enemy] is armed more or less, and to know thus whether one is ready or not, whether it is fitting to attack or to defend oneself, and also whether it is fitting to discharge the cannon. Nothing is more useful than this instrument."[121]

In the neighborhood of 1630 or a little later, Father Schall expressed himself in these words: "Many erroneous explanations have been given in antiquity of the nature and the sinuous tracing of the Milky Way.

Recently the telescope has revealed that one is dealing here with a strip of innumerable small stars which are collected among themselves, as if they were so many nebulae in Cancer. Since, besides, one is dealing with a formation of collected small stars which the human eye is not adequate to discern, so it is that they now form a spectacle of this kind."[122] And again: "When one observes the stars with the telescope, they are much more numerous than at ordinary times; not only is their number tens of times greater, but their light is very brilliant."[123]

A few years later Rho, after having noted that all astronomers, ancient and modern, always made use of instruments, continues then in these words: "But the forces of the eye are limited and the principles of instruments are not infinite. In these last years, a famous mathematician of the regions of the Occident has manufactured a telescope with which one can see distant things as if they were near and small things as if they were great. The principle thereof is very delicate and the use very vast. Concerning this see the special treatise {Schall's}." Then he signalizes the discoveries made possible by the telescope in the field of astronomy. With it one sees innumerable heaps of stars which before one did not see. Before, Saturn was a single body; now instead one sees it "three-bodied," that is, accompanied by two satellites which travel around it, above, below, to the right, to the left, at times visible, at times invisible. With the telescope one sees Jupiter always attended by four satellites which travel rapidly around it and which change position continually. Venus does not have satellites but has phases the same as those of the moon. Many small stars around the sun, when looked at with the telescope, seem so many black points of which one does not yet know the nature.[124]

Farther on, in the same work, Rho speaks of the Milky Way, and here is what he says about it: "What is the Milky Way? The ancients, thinking that the Milky Way was not composed of stars, did not put it in the heaven of the constellations, but, believing that its light might be similar to the light clouds upon which the sun is reflected, put it under the heaven of the moon and called it a permanent nebula. Today, however, one no longer speaks thus. After the invention of the telescope, observing the heavens with it, one has seen clearly that {the Milky Way} is composed of innumerable small stars."[125]

24. *The Galilean Discoveries in* The Sphere *by Schreck* (c. 1628)

Immediately after this treatise by Schall on the telescope, Schreck also (after 1623, the year of his arrival at Peking, and before 1630, the year of his death—therefore probably about 1628) composed a treatise on *Abridged Theory on Measures of the Sky* or *The Sphere*,[126] in which he remembered his old colleague of the Academy of the Lincei, even if, for the reason already explained, he did not name him. Treating, in fact, of the motion of the revolution which Venus, Mercury, and the sun complete in a year, he asked whether, since they complete the same revolution in a year, there can still be distances between them. In giving the reply he reported first of all the opinions of the ancients, which he qualified without further ado as "fantastic,"[127] since they held that the two stars were either above the fourth heaven, that of the sun, or under it. Then he added: "But in these late years a celebrated mathematician of the kingdoms of the Occident in order to observe Venus has constructed a lens which permits one to see afar. {With this instrument} sometimes {the star} is obscure, sometimes it is completely illuminated, sometimes it is illuminated either in the superior quarter or in the inferior quarter. This proves that Venus is a satellite of the sun and travels around it. When the planet is distant, contrary to what happens with the moon, a half of it is illuminated, which proves that then it is above the sun. When it is full it appears very small. When it is not seen this means that it is under the sun. When, finally, it is on the sides of the sun, one has the two quarters. The same may be said of the very small Mercury which is exceedingly close to the sun and of which one does not easily discern the luminosity or obscurity; also it moves like Venus and one measures it in virtue of the same principle."[128]

Further on, Schreck also described the sunspots and the telescope in these terms: "On the sun there are spots of various sizes: one, two, or three or four, but no more. They are found always above a line running east and west across the sun. They constantly follow the same trajectory and disappear after fourteen days. When the first spots are finished, others take their place. The largest spots can cause the light of the sun to be dimmed. When the spots were first discovered they were thought to be Venus, perhaps, or Mercury; but the trajectories did not agree. Observed recently with the telescope, they have, on the one hand, been seen not to be part of the body of the sun, but, on the other hand, not distant from the sun, like red clouds; but to be exactly in front of it. What they are is unknown."[129]

25. *Already the Idea of Constructing Telescopes* (c. 1630)

The missionaries were not content with reading abstract descriptions of these discoveries. They wished to descend, as soon as possible, to the level of practical application. An occasion came on June 21, 1629, with an eclipse of the sun. On the preceding day exponents of the three rival astronomies—the Chinese, the Mohammedan, and the European, the last represented by the missionaries—were required to put in writing their predictions of the next day's eclipse. The traditional mathematicians foretold that it would start at 10:30 and end at 12:30, lasting two hours. Instead, the eclipse occurred at 11:30 and lasted only two minutes, just as the missionaries predicted. There was great excitement in responsible circles. Two days later, June 23, the Privy Council presented an unfavorable report of the performance of the traditional mathematicians to the emperor and a grand eulogy of European astronomy. About two months later, August 29, the Ministry of Rites presented a detailed explanation of how a reform of the calendar might be undertaken, a reform, incidentally, which had not been made in approximately three and a half centuries. On September 1 an imperial edict was issued entrusting the reform to the missionaries and their pupils. On September 13, the director, an exemplary Christian, the celebrated Dr. Paul Hsü Kuang-ch'i, whom we have already met, proposed, on the advice of Schreck, a vast program of translation of scientific books and a complete outfit of scientific instruments. He envisaged the translation of books on arithmetic, geometry, hydraulics, music, optics, astronomy, and so forth; and the construction of six great quadrants, three devices for measuring angles in all directions, three armillary spheres, an instrument for representing eclipses, a celestial sphere, a terrestrial globe, three ordinary quadrants, three other quadrants for measuring sidereal time, three clocks, and, as will interest us, three telescopes in copper, iron, and wood to observe eclipses of the planets. These telescopes were to be so well constructed that they would cost six *taels* apiece, apart from the price of the lenses.[130]

Already on October 25, 1631, observations were made with a telescope.[131]

In that same year and in following years some telescopes arrived in several cities of the province of Fukien brought there by the missionaries Andrew Rudomina, S.J. and Julius Aleni, S.J.[132]

26. The Galilean Discoveries in Korea (1631) and in Japan (before 1638)

In 1631 there arrived at Peking a Korean ambassador called by the Chinese Chêng Tou-yüan 鄭斗源. This man disembarked at Tengchow in Shantung where at that time a Christian general, Ignatius Sun Yüan-hua, 孫元化, was governor. In fact, in the years 1629–30 the Manchus had already forced the Great Wall at three points and were menacing Peking. Then two Christians, Leo Li Chih-tsao and Paul Hsü Kuang-ch'i, mentioned above, persuaded the court to appeal to the Portuguese of Macao to send men and cannon. For the second or third time, then, Gonçalo Teixeira, 公沙的西勞, in the company of Father John Rodriguez, The Interpreter, whom we have already met, came, at the head of five or six artillerymen who brought about a dozen cannon. Our ambassador was acquainted with Father Rodriguez there and so wrote a letter to him in which he asked several things about the calendar. The reply which Father Rodriguez sent, in Chinese, to the interpreter of the ambassador is still preserved at the library of the University of Seoul, and has been published by *The Historical Journal of Japan,*[133] vol. XLIV. He expressed himself in these words: "Inasmuch as my fellow citizens love long voyages we have come to China where we have been received magnificently and where, in order to show our gratitude a little, we have offered some firearms. Having arrived in the eastern part of Manchuria, and having found there some learned men, we have offered to them our {Chinese} translations. Who would ever have thought that they would consider them so important? On the World Map China occupies the center, as they saw. Truly, on the terrestrial globe any country whatever can be the center. When the Chinese saw this map and saw the Occidentals, then they knew that the earth is great and that the countries are many. {They knew} that in the Orient as in the Occident there are *saints* and sages who belong to the same race, reason in the same manner, and have the same intelligence, and therefore apply themselves to study with all the intensity permitted to man. This one already knew, in the large, from the writings of Fu Hsi, Yao, Shun, King Wên, the Duke of Chou, Confucius, and even from the books of the Buddhists and the Taoists. {In China it is said:} 'The Supreme Ultimate produces the two forms, the forms are divided into four images, the images are divided into eight trigrams, and the trigrams produce heaven, earth, man, and things.'[134] According to the Occidental interpretation, the Great Ultimate is something material, is matter without intelligence and without consciousness.[135] Unless there is the infinite, omnipotent, wise, and intelligent factor, how could it ever produce things? Then, as for the political doctrine of the three principal duties, of the five ordinary virtues, and of the five relations,[136] it agrees with that of our kingdom. Besides this science of the things of the world there is also the science of the things of heaven {=God}, which tradition was lost when Shih Huang-ti burnt the books {in 213 B.C.}. China, which believes only in the ancients, sometimes has fallen into error or has changed {doctrine}. Occidental science, on the other hand, from antiquity down until today, confronts {doctrines} continually and does not stop before arriving at the source. Then, as for the doctrines of Buddhism and Taoism, if we may discuss them according to the truth, one sees immediately that they are erroneous. How should they be worthy of being believed? If man who is born into the world has had a beginning, he will have also an end. But the beginning, whence does it come? And the end, whither does it go? Is it ever possible not to see clearly in a question of such great importance? This is a point which is discussed by the three religions, but I beg you to give great importance to it and to be very watchful of it. Astronomy, on the other hand, {in China} is very elementary, and consequently there are errors in the calendar. There has always been the desire to correct the calendar, from the times of the Han and the T'ang on. If even the great astronomer Kuo Shou-ching, under the Mongols, did not find the cause of these errors, how should it be possible to avoid them? Now that the emperor has given us the responsibility to make this correction, if one can do all these translations we can guarantee that there will never again be any errors. It is impossible to exhaust in a few words the doctrinal particulars of astronomy. We shall speak of them again in detail when we have the time for it. There is something already in *The Origin of the Commission of the Calendar*. It is necessary first to familiarize oneself therewith and to grasp its sense by means of the illustrations without my speaking here of any problem in particular.

Awaiting instructions. With greetings. John Rodriguez."[137]

So it was that when the ambassador re-entered Korea on August 9, 1631, he took with him books and scientific instruments received as gifts from Father Rodriguez. Among other things, he took to his country two books on astronomy which must have been Ricci's *Treatise on Heaven and Earth*,[138] and Diaz's *Sphere*[139] or Schreck's *Abridged Theory on Measures of the Sky*,[140] where, as we have observed previously, Galileo's discoveries are spoken of. He carried, besides, two books on the telescope, one of which was certainly Schall's, mentioned above. Among the scientific instruments, besides clocks and European cannon, there was a telescope or "mirror of a thousand *li*,"[141] given as a gift by Rodriguez.[142] The telescope could have been worth 300 or 400 Korean dollars; with it, it is said, one could see to 100 *li* or almost 40 kilometers the smallest objects.[143] In such manner, just when Galileo's trial was on the point of beginning, he, without knowing it, saw his telescope introduced through the work of the Jesuit missionaries of Peking as far as Korea.

From Korea these inventions did not delay in crossing the short stretch of sea and passing to Japan, still before the death of the great Pisan. It would be interesting to study the influence which Galileo had, by means of the scientific books printed in Chinese by the Jesuit missionaries of Peking, on Seki Kòwa 関孝和, whom the Japanese call the Japanese Newton, not only because like Newton he was born in the same year as that of Galileo's death, but because in fact he was one of the greatest mathematical geniuses of the Land of the Rising Sun.[144] What is certain is that in 1638 the telescope had arrived at Nagasaki, since on the southeast side of the city in that year there was placed on a hill an *Observatory for Foreigners,* or Observatory for spying from a distance the coming of foreigners to Japan, furnished with a telescope which permitted the seeing of the arrival of foreign ships and the sending then of a boat with black flag to announce the matter immediately to the Office of Voyages.[145]

Returning to China, one finds allusions to the telescope both in the work *Reply to Questions of the Guest*[146] (1632) by the Christian Cosma Chu Tsung-yüan 朱宗元 and in Schall's exposition of *The Double Stellar Hemisphere* (1634).[147]

27. Two Parallel Texts of Schall (c. 1634)

Probably towards 1634 Father Schall published two books in Chinese: *Introduction to the European Calendar,*[148] and *Divergences of European Astronomy from Chinese Astronomy.*[149] In both these publications he had occasion to describe scientific instruments. He justly remarked: "Observational instruments are to the astronomer what the plumbline or square is to the engineer. That is, they are indispensable." Then he indicated the chief scientific instruments known up until his time: the celestial globe, the armillary sphere, the ecliptic armilla, the quadrant, the sextant, the gnomen, and so forth. Then he continued in these words: "The most marvelous and most perfect instrument is the recently invented telescope. It is an instrument even more necessary than the others for observing the heavens. By means of it one can give the exact minute of a solar eclipse, one can observe the phases of Venus, one can see the four small stars on the sides of Jupiter; with it {one can observe} that Saturn is cylindrical-shaped with two small stars on its sides, that the Pleiades contain more than thirty stars, that those of the nebula in Cancer, even the least luminous, not only appear tens of times more numerous, but are clearly distinct from one another and have a scintillating light. What an admirable instrument this is!" In the above text, repeated with light stylistic retouches in the other publication, Father Schall added: "But this instrument invented recently in the Occident did not exist a century ago."

The student of Sinology, or even the simple Sinological dilettante, may be interested in verifying the perfect parallelism of ideas, expressed almost with the same words, in the two above-mentioned publications of Schall. Only the slightest differences of shading permit one to distinguish one text from the other. Naturally, both texts are by the same pen, or, more properly, brush: that, probably, of the missionary-astronomer's Chinese secretary.[150]

So that the reader can judge for himself this paralellism, I willingly put it before his eyes in the following double column:

Introduction to the European Calendar (f. 36a) (Vatican Library, General Collection, Orient. III, 244³⁻⁴)	Divergences of European Astronomy from Chinese Astronomy (f. 21a–b) (Vatican Library, General Collection, Orient. III, 244¹)
而其最奇巧者，則 近時所製遠鏡，尤為 窺天要具. 用之能詳 日食分秒, 能見太白 有上下弦, 能見歲星 旁四小星, 又填星為 橢形, 旁附有兩小星, 昴宿星三十餘, 鬼宿 中之積尸氣, 以至 光體微渺之星, 用此 奚蕾多數十倍, 抑 且界限分明, 光耀璀 璨. 噫造器至此, 異 甚矣	而其最巧最奇, 則 所製遠鏡, 更為窺天 要具. 用之能詳日食分 秒, 能觀太白有上下 弦, 能見歲星旁四小 星, 填星為橢形, 旁附 有兩小星, 昴宿有三 十餘, 鬼宿中之積尸 氣, 以至體微光渺之 星, 用此所見, 奚蕾多 數十倍, 又且界限分 明, 光芒璀璨然. 此亦 西洋近時新增之器, 百年前未有也

In regard to the Milky Way, Schall noted: "What is the Milky Way? The ancients not believing that the Milky Way was composed of stars, did not put it in the heaven of the constellations. Thinking that their light was similar to the light clouds which reflect the sun, they said that they were constant nebulae under the heaven of the moon. Today, however, one thinks differently. After the invention of the telescope, using this instrument to make observations, one has seen clearly that {the Milky Way is composed} of innumerable small stars."[151] And in another of his books he observed: "That that which anciently was called the Milky Way was composed of nebulae is an error. The new astronomy using the telescope to make its observations has begun to know that it is formed by the assemblage of innumerable small stars, similar to a heap of nebulae. This is enough to show the futility of the former error."[152] Already in 1634 he had observed, speaking evidently of the Milky Way: "Formerly one doubted that they were stars and therefore one called [them] nebulae, but now, observed with the telescope, {one knows that they all are stars.}"[153]

28. *The Telescope is Explained and Offered to the Emperor* (1634)

Towards the end of 1634, the Christian Dr. Peter Li T'ien-ching 李天經[154] (1579–1659), who had succeeded Paul Hsü Kuang-ch'i, dead the preceding year, as director of the Astronomical Bureau, was accused before the Emperor of having been the only one to use the telescope. The worst hypotheses were permitted in those days. Thus it was that on November 4 of that same year he presented to the throne a memorial in which, exculpating himself of the charge brought against him, he gave an accurate description of the telescope. Here is the text: "The telescope was invented in the Far West; it is an instrument of the new {i.e., European} astronomy, for the purpose of seeing where other instruments do not see. It is very useful. I have previously indicated [the plan] of constructing one of these. When the solar and stellar clocks are finished, I shall present to Your Majesty the three instruments at the same time." After having described the first two instruments, this is what he says about the telescope: "The telescope has a diameter of a little more than 1 inch {=35 millimeters}. The light of the stars penetrates into it and reaches all the way down to the man's eye. This instrument can individuate two stars so close that the human eye does not distinguish their outlines. It can see those stars which are so small that the eye discerns them with difficulty. When two stars are distant the one from the other by a half a degree, that is, 30 minutes according to the new astronomy, and therefore cannot be observed either by measuring instruments or by the eye, the telescope can observe both of them clearly, because it has a capacity of a little more than a half a degree, which constitutes its measure. However, two stars distant by more than a half a degree cannot be observed together.

"For example, the three stars of Orion, λ and two φ, which are at a distance of 37 minutes, cannot be seen together. Two stars under the western column of the five planets, which are distant by more than 44 minutes, cannot be seen together. Is it not evident, then, that the measure of this instrument is a little more than a half a degree?

"This is why on the nights of October 15 and 22, together with the clerks of my department, I observed in my bureau Jupiter in Cancer, distant almost half a degree from the nebula; Jupiter, flashing with light but of very small size, would not have been observable without the telescope.

" If I alone used this telescope, it was because I wished that all might make by themselves the same observation, might see with clear proof that the nebula is formed by the uniting together of several tens of small stars, and might perceive that, since Jupiter and the nebula were able to be observed together with the telescope, there was no error in their conjunction."[155]

This memorial was presented on November 4, 1634. On the seventh came the imperial rescript which said: "We have well understood that the telescope is only an instrument for reaching where other instruments do not reach. When all the instruments are finished and ready for presentation to Us, advise the Ministry of Rites."[156]

On December 19 of the same year, 1634, the same Li T'ien-ching presented a new memorial announcing that the three instruments of which he spoke in the previous memorial were ready. In it he recalled that on November 22, 1632, Hsü Kuang-ch'i had asked permission to construct these instruments. Now, it was added, they were constructed. The memorial, therefore, described the nature, method of use, and placement of the instruments: the solar clock should be placed south, the stellar clock north. Then he spoke again about the telescope: "In compliance with Your Majesty's request, I have already sufficiently explained the optic tube, called also telescope. It is constructed as follows: at the two ends are lenses separated from each other by several empty tubes inserted in one another so that they can be shortened or lengthened at will according to whether the object to be seen is near or far. With such an instrument one can observe not only the sky but also objects several *li* distant as if they were under the observer's eye. It is very useful for watching the enemy in cannon's range. This instrument, brought by James Rho and John Schall from their kingdoms, was afterwards decorated for presentation to Your Majesty."[157]

Finally, a third memorial presented on December 28, 1634, described precisely: "Previously, on the 24th of the current month of December I explained to two eunuchs, Lu Wei-ning and Wei Kuo-chêng, who came to the bureau to see the telescope, the method of lengthening and shortening it and how it should be placed. I beg, therefore, to be able to present a telescope to Your Majesty in compliance with your previous orders.

"Objects presented: a telescope, two copper guards for the telescope, a cloth of silk brocade, a box of the finest yellow silk for the telescope, a wooden stand."[158]

The date of the memorial is expressed thus:

崇禎七年十一月初九日具題恭進, 十二日
奉〇旨, 知道了, 該衙門知道[159]

The telescope offered at the end of 1634 with so much formality must have pleased the Son of Heaven much since another document informs us that by his special request Fathers Rho and Schall made him two other instruments which they presented him on September 19, 1635.[160]

Probably presentations of similar gifts were renewed again in following years.[161] We know, for example, that in 1637 Father Schall, when he presented the scientific books translated into Chinese, had already finished making several astronomical instruments, a solar clock, a stellar clock, and a telescope.[162] We know besides that on December 29, 1639, Father Francis Sambiasi[163] offered to the emperor a *Map of the Stars*[164] and a *Geographical Map*,[165] to which he added other small gifts, an Occidental harpsichord, a kind of small organ, a clock which sounded the hours, a convex lens for concentrating solar rays, a clepsydra, a white parrot with a large crest from the Indian Ocean, and even a telescope. In the memorial which accompanied these gifts, Sambiasi introduced himself in these words: "I, your subject, am a humble literatus from the

Far West, who dedicate myself to the study of philosophy, occupy myself with serving heaven {=God} and loving men, purify myself, and apply myself to virtue. In company with my companions Matthew Ricci and others, whose coming started with the times of Wan Li and continued thereafter, I have made in three years a sea-voyage of 80,000 *li* and have come in order to admire this kingdom from which we are grateful for so many benefits, among others that of having been conceded a place for burial of the dead and soil for the living." To show their gratitude, the missionaries dedicated themselves to the correction of the calendar, wanted to aid China in exploiting the mines, in establishing commerce with the Occident, and in yet other matters.[166]

29. *The Great Astronomer "Chialilêo"* (c. 1640)

We come thus to about the year 1640 when, under the editorship of the same Father Schall, there appeared a short *History of Occidental Astronomers*, in Chinese *Li-fa hsi chuan*.[167] Because of the historical character of the publication, this time the personages were phoneticized in Chinese according to the constant usage of that people in regard to foreign proper names of persons and places. In this book, then, Ptolemy 多祿某, Alphonso X 亞而封所 king of Castile and León, Copernicus 哥白尼, Simon {Stevin} 西滿, Magini 麻日諾, Vieta 未葉大, Tycho Brahe 第谷, and finally Galileo are mentioned.[168] Here is what is said of the great Italian astronomer: "After Tycho's death the telescope was invented by means of which the smallest stars of the heavens were rendered visible. Thirty years ago—thus this was written toward 1640 —*Chia-li-lê-o* 加利勒阿 {that is, Galileo} made a new map of the heavens and made known in a publication that which no astronomer had reached in several thousands of years. There arose then many scholars who made this teaching better and better known. Thus it was known that Jupiter is surrounded by four small stars which travel {around it} with great rapidity; it was known besides that Saturn is surrounded by two other small stars, that Venus has phases, and so forth, things all unheard of until then. Besides, Occidental travelers who have gone to 80° north have reported that winter is reduced to a continuous night; those, on the other hand, who have made the circuit of the world have reported that at more than 40° south the antarctic polar star is completely visible. In this way the stellar map is now completed."[169]

30. Did the Jesuits Hide the Heliocentric System from the Chinese?

Among certain modern authors it is fashionable to accuse the Jesuits of the seventeenth century of having hidden from the Chinese Galileo's discoveries, and thus the heliocentric system, and of having adhered to the Ptolemaic system supported by the Scholastics. If one listens to these censors, just at the moment when the Chinese were placed in the current of Occidental science, this science was out of fashion and antiquated. This, naturally, because they were priests who could not say that Galileo was right when he had been twice condemned by the Church.

Professor Duyvendak himself, the great Sinologue recently deceased, of the University of Leiden, in the pages which with so much courtesy he wanted to dedicate to the first Italian edition of my *Galileo in Cina*, in *T'oung Pao*[170] seems, however, to have wished to fill the rôle of authorized mouthpiece of these critics. He writes at the end of his review, after having mentioned, as I say below, that between the two opposing interpretations of the system of the world the Jesuits preferred the compromise proposed by neither one of them, but by the Protestant Tycho Brahe: "The Jesuits in China propagated his cause (=Galileo's cause) as long as this was feasible. As churchmen this was no longer possible for them after the final condemnation . . . The impossibility for the Jesuits, the mediators of Western science in China, to accept Galileo's heliocentric theory is a matter of immense cultural significance. It meant that China, when it received Western science, received it in a form that, in principle, was already antiquated. It was cheated out of the most startling discovery that man had yet made, a discovery which, happily followed up as it was by men like Newton, may be regarded as the starting point of the phenomenal development in science and the revolution of man's thought that characterized the following centuries in Europe. 'Modern' science in China remained essentially mediaeval; never were Chinese scholars faced with the appalling vision of 'T'ien-hsia' flying through space as a mere speck of dust."[171]

This picture by the eminent Sinologue seems a little overdone, and I do not believe that it reflects objectively the attitude of the Jesuits toward the Galilean discoveries or towards the heliocentric system. What we have said hitherto proves that the Jesuit missionaries in China exerted every effort to make known to the Chinese in the shortest time possible Galileo's discoveries. Then, as for the heliocentric system, it is necessary to note that the learned did not accept Galileo's conclusions until several decades after his death. Only in the second half of the seventeenth century did opinions, until then conflicting, orient themselves in the sense of the Copernican system. It was especially in the eighteenth century that the majority of Occidental scientists accepted the heliocentric system; thus also did the Jesuits. But this period extends beyond the limits which I have set for myself, desiring here to treat only of the time before the death of the great astronomer (1642). Moreover, even during this time, when one could only speak hypothetically, texts are not lacking which prove that the Jesuits were not then so anti-Copernican as these critics would like to make one believe.

As we have seen above (note 39), the great Clavius before his death in 1612 had decided that after Galileo's discoveries a change in opinions on the constitution of the universe was required: "Videant Astronomi quo pacto orbes coelestes constituendi sint ut haec phaenomena {the phenomena brought to notice by Galileo} possint salvari." ["Let astronomers see how the celestial spheres must be constituted in order to save these phenomena."]When theologians were of the opinion that, following the Holy Fathers, it was necessary to interpret in the literal sense certain texts of the Bible which seemed to say that the earth is immobile and that the sun travels around the earth, Cardinal Bellarmine, a member of the Holy Office, in order to avoid "irritating all the philosophers and Scholastic theologians," and "hurting the Holy Faith by saying that the Sacred Scriptures erred," on April 12, 1615, recommended to Father Paul Anthony Foscarini, provincial of the Carmelites in Calabria, to be satisfied with presenting the Galilean doctrines as a hypothesis, which in fact it was at that time, and not as certain doctrine. "It seems to me that Your Paternity and Mr. Galileo would do prudently to content yourselves with speaking *ex suppositione* and not absolutely, as I have always believed Copernicus to have spoken . . . This is enough to the mathematician." In case, however, that "there should be true demonstration that the sun is in the center of the world and the earth in the third heaven and that the sun does not travel around the earth but the earth travels around the sun, then it would be necessary to proceed with much consideration in explaining the Scriptures which seem contrary and rather to say that we do not understand them than to say that that is false which one demonstrates. But I shall not believe that there is such a demonstration until it has been demonstrated."[172]

Towards 1633, as I have pointed out,[173] it is said that other Jesuits, among them the encyclopaedic Athanasius Kircher and Clavius' successor to the chair of mathematics at the Roman College, Christopher Grienberger, had nothing to say against Copernicus, rather were not at all far removed from him, or at least were inclined to admit his hypothesis. This for Europe.

As for China, then, let us remember before all, as we have seen above, how convinced a Copernican was the Bohemian Wenceslaus Kirwitzer,[174] who was one of those missionaries who on April 16, 1618, departed from Lisbon for the Middle Kingdom, along with Trigault. He who could have been one of the first and one of the most convinced defenders of the new ideas died prematurely in 1626, when the work of correcting the calendar had not yet begun. There is proof that, a little after Galileo's death, two Polish Jesuits, Michael Boym and Nicholas Smogolenski, perhaps influenced by their love of the fatherland that they had in common with Copernicus, recommended strongly the theory of their compatriot. The former, in December 1646, sent from Macao to Peking the *Tabulae Rudolphinae* edited by Kepler, which he called a book "unique and best for calculating total and partial eclipses and the movements of the heavens."[175] The latter seems to have taught the new astronomical theories at Nanking around 1645, or even earlier, and to have made some proselytes among the Chinese scholars.[176]

Let us here call attention to an important text by James Rho which openly alludes both to Galileo and to the heliocentric system, which, however, he did not accept. Here is this text, part of which one reads with Fang Hao:[177] "How does one explain the motion of the *primum mobile* heaven? The answers are two. There is he {=Galileo} who says: The *primum mobile* is not the sun which completes its revolution in a day, traveling around the earth and dragging all the other heavens towards the west. One who stands on the earth and looks at the stars believes that they move towards the left; nevertheless this is not the proper motion of the stars since they do not complete their revolution in a day and a night; but the earth, the air, and the fire form a single globe which goes from the west to the east and completes its revolution in a day. It is like one who is making a voyage in a boat and looks at the bank, the trees, and so forth. He does not have the impression that it is he who proceeds but thinks that it is the bank which proceeds. For the same reason, the man who stands on the earth has the impression that the stars go toward the west. The earth's motion spares the many motions of the heavens, as the earth's small revolution spares the great revolutions of the heavens.

"However, ancient and modern scientists have thought that really this is not the true explanation. In fact, the earth is the center of the various heavens, and the center, like the pivot of a waggon, is fixed and immobile. Besides, if it is true that one who stands in a boat sees the bank as if it were moving, why not concede that those who stand on the bank see that the boat is moving? Pure comparison, thus, is not a proof.

"And now here is the true explanation. The earth is immobile. The *primum mobile* heaven is the highest sphere of the stars, which has its pole and has its proper motion, while the heavens englobed by it, having both the poles and being totally dependent on the *primum mobile*, cannot but move together with it. Let there be, for example, a man who proceeds on a ship, or an ant that proceeds on a millstone. Although having a proper motion of their own, they cannot but follow, also, the motion of the ship or of the millstone.

"To ask the thickness, the nature, or the color of the *primum mobile*, or the nature or the color of the heavens, is to ask questions which relate to physics and do not relate to astronomy. See, apropos of this, the translation of Aristotle's *De Coelo* (1628). Astronomers are satisfied to affirm the existence of mobile heavens, of small orbits, and of non-concentric circles, and so forth, in order to be able to make equal the degrees of the stars. They do not pretend to say that all this corresponds to reality. This is because there are divergent opinions. We, here, occupy ourselves only with observations and calculations. There is no need to discuss at length in order to know who is right and who is wrong."[178]

Shortly before this text, the same Rho had written: "Without doubt, the ancient and the modern {astronomy} do not agree. The ancients said: the earth's center is the center of the orbit of each of the five planets in their movement. The moderns, on the other hand, say: it is the sun which is the center of the five planets. The ancients said: every planet has its proper heaven and these heavens, which are solid, involve one another in such a way that they cannot meet each other. The moderns, on the other hand, say: in as much as the orbits can interpenetrate one another, and thus meet one another, the heavens are not necessarily solid. The ancients said: Saturn, Jupiter, and Mars are always outside of the solar system. The moderns, on the other hand, say: sometimes Mars is in the solar system."[179]

And, speaking in general, Rho was not afraid to put this question: "Since the ancients said that the heavens were hard, solid, and unyielding to light, is it not openly to go against the true astronomy of the ancient scientists to maintain with modern astronomers that the orbit of Mars cuts the sun's orbit?" as happens to those who support the system invented by Tycho Brahe? To which he courageously answers: "Ever since antiquity, in astronomical observations, one has been constrained to base oneself on the {phenomena} of the sky. If what one had constructed independently agreed perfectly with what minute observation revealed, one then was treating of the true astronomy. If it had not been thus, how would it have been possible to adhere with tenacity to the ancients and contradict {the phenomena} of the sky? And here is the reason. In kind, the observations of the ancients were a bit simple, all the more because they were based on what the eye saw. But today's observations are tens of times more precise, and, if one uses the telescope, are hundreds of times more precise than those of the ancients.

Thus, if one leaves the ancients to follow the moderns, it is certainly
not for the purpose of representing oneself as more intelligent than
they, nor of deviating madly from the high road."[180]

All these texts, which are of 1637, prove that even for the period
before Galileo's death, when in Europe itself scientists were quite far
from agreement in admitting the heliocentrism of Copernicus and
Galileo, it is not possible to maintain with Duyvendak that "never were
Chinese scholars faced with the appalling vision of the 'T'ien-hsia'
flying through space as a mere speck of dust."

We, therefore, shall conclude this question with the observation
that, besides the difficulties already noted and explained, the Jesuits
believed that the time had not yet come to contradict too openly the
Chinese who from time immemorial, no less than the Europeans, had
made the earth the center of the universe. This is what Professor B.
Szcześniak, of the University of Notre Dame, Indiana, has us note in
a comment on exactly this question of the introduction of the theory
of Copernicus into China. He wrote, then, in 1945: "There seems to
be no doubt that the Jesuits in China accepted the superiority of the
Copernican system, though they did not proclaim it openly. Tactical
reasons did not allow them to declare themselves suddenly in favour of
the new theory. The more so because the Copernican doctrine was in
conflict with the traditional Chinese science that made the earth the
centre of the universe. This point proved a mutual base of collaboration
between the Chinese and European astronomers in Peking. A sudden
rupture with the traditional philosophy and science of China by sub-
stituting for it the heliocentric system would have encountered a vio-
lent resistance and might have caused additional difficulties in spreading
Christianity. Even in Europe a quasi-revolution was caused by Copernicus. In these circumstances the Ptolemaic theory was certainly more
opportune, and the solar one would have had no practical advantages.
The prediction of solar eclipses and the calculation of the calendar
could be sufficiently exact by the use of the Greek theory. The Copern -
can theory also required proper cultural conditions, and one could
hardly say if they existed in China."[181]

All these reasons put together cause us to be less severe towards the
Jesuit scientists in China during all the seventeenth century and especially during the period before the year of Galileo's death (1642).

Epilogue: The Jesuits and the Condemnation of Galileo

The texts examined in this study all antedate Galileo's death. Did the astronomer ever know how zealously and perhaps unexpectedly Portuguese, German, and Italian missionaries in China brought his marvelous discoveries to the attention of the Chinese? Today we can certainly answer: No. In any case, how could he have known? After 1626 Kirwitzer was dead. Schreck, who insisted until 1622 on having the Pisan's eclipse calculations, was already taken away from science in 1630. Almost all these texts were in Chinese books, and although several copies of these books were at Rome, where they are still preserved, nobody there at the time could read them. If the idea of rediscovering and evaluating these texts,[182] which until then nobody had signalized or translated, did not occur to me until the occasion of the tercentenary of Galileo's death, 1942, we should not wonder that Galileo did not know anything about them.

If some chance Sinologue had informed Galileo, he might have changed his mind about who his true antagonists were. It is known that at the end of his life, because of the tension between him and Father Scheiner, there was a desire to make the great astronomer believe that he ought to see the cause of his misfortunes in the Jesuits. Even during the present tercentenary of his death an author has written that two Jesuits, Grassi and Scheiner, denounced Galileo before the Holy Office.

If this author meant to allude to the injunction of 1616, one must say that his allegation is absolutely false. Father Grassi engaged in no controversy with Galileo before 1618. Father Scheiner, who at that time was a professor of mathematics at Ingolstadt, did not come to Rome until 1624, eight years after the famous injunction.

If this author meant to refer to the final sentence of 1633, his allegation is false and calumnious, in so far as it concerns Father Grassi. Grassi wrote thus to Jerome Bardi on September 22, 1633: "As for Mr. Galileo's displeasure, I tell you most sincerely that I, too, am displeased. I have always had more love for him than he has for me. And last year at Rome {thus during the trial which led to Galileo's condemnation} when I was requested to give my opinion on his book on the motion of the earth, I took the utmost care to allay minds harshly disposed toward him and to render them open to conviction of the strength of his arguments, so much so, indeed, that certain people who supposed me to have been offended by Galileo, and thus, perhaps, not very well disposed, marveled at my solicitude. But he has ruined himself by being so much in love with his own genius, and by having no respect for others. One should not wonder that everybody conspires to damn him."[183]

Father Scheiner, on the other hand, was vaguely accused by three of his contemporaries of having blown on the flame. Gabriel Naudé and James Gaffarel, both of them French, and Mattias Bernegger, an Austrian, reported in 1633 and 1640 the gossip that Scheiner cooperated in the condemnation of Galileo and was one of the chief instigators. "Le P. Scheiner, Jésuite, luy a joué ce tour, *ut creditur*" ["Father Scheiner, a Jesuit, has played this trick on him, *as is believed*"], Gaffarel wrote in May 1633.[184]

Since it would take too much space to sift these three testimonies, I must confine myself to the observation that even if it were proved, and it has not been proved, that Father Scheiner actively and really cooperated in Galileo's misfortune, Father Scheiner neither was, nor represented, the Society of Jesus as a whole. In any case, to one Jesuit who may have fought the great astronomer, one may oppose several others, like the missionaries in China, who did everything possible to propagate knowledge of Galileo's discoveries among Chinese scholars and in the imperial court itself.

The missionaries in China, furthermore, would probably have supported him even more if his affairs at Rome had not become complicated. We may feel almost certain that had it not been for the injunction of February 26, 1616, which was not widely known anyhow,[185] and, particularly, had it not been for the sentence of 1633, the Jesuits in China would have followed him not only in his discoveries, which, as we have proved, they did, within a very short time and with the utmost enthusiasm, but also, in all probability, in the conclusions he drew from them in favor of the heliocentric system. It was because of the known condemnations of the Holy Office that the missionaries stopped in the middle of the road as far as Galileo was concerned. Nor can any reasonable person blame them for this. Their first duty was to obey the decisions of Rome. They preserved their scientific sympathies for the great astronomer, for his discoveries, and perhaps even for his conclusions. But in the interpretations of the new phenomena which they published in their scientific writings they remained at the halfway point. Like the mathematicians at Ingolstadt and the Roman College, they preferred, between the two opposed systems of the world—the Ptolemaic interpretation and the Copernican interpretation—the compromise proposed by Tycho Brahe. They preferred, that is, to think of the other planets as moving around the sun, but of the sun as moving around the earth. Hence, they left the earth immobile at the center of the universe, and yet gave the same explanation of phenomena, fundamentally, as Kepler gave. Anyhow, the decisive proof of the heliocentric system did not come until many years after Galileo.

Given, therefore, this complex of circumstances, it seems to me that the Jesuit scientists in China did for Galileo all that can reasonably be expected of men who lived in that age. While he was repudiated, persecuted, and twice condemned, they cooperated effectively in his favor by making his discoveries known to the extreme limits of the world. In truth, they deserved well of Galileo and his cause. This little-known page of the vast repercussion of Galileo's discoveries in such distant lands was, in my opinion, worthy of being recorded in a publication of the Pontifical Gregorian University, heir and continuation of that Roman College which received Galileo within its walls in May 1611, and solemnly fêted the great Tuscan astronomer, congratulating him for his recent discoveries.

APPENDIX

THE FIRST EUROPEAN DOCUMENT ON THE CHINESE
CALENDAR (AUGUST 1612)

In the preceding pages we have seen the truly astonishing insistence
with which the missionary-scientists of China for many years requested
Galileo Galilei to collaborate in their scientific work.

The reason for this insistence was that the Chinese calendar, of immense social and political importance in the seventeenth century, had
been wrong for about three hundred years. Nobody could make the
necessary and urgent corrections. The teaching of the Arabs, received
by the Chinese in the thirteenth century, was all lost, except for astronomical tables and empirical methods of predicting eclipses. Since,
thus, the whole theoretical part of astronomy had disappeared centuries
earlier, the errors could not be eliminated for the simple reason that
nobody knew how to find them.

Ricci, whose scientific preparation was that of a student at the
Roman College toward the close of the sixteenth century, reached the
Middle Kingdom in 1583. To win the hearts of the Chinese he began
to occupy himself with scientific matters, and the mandarins of the
empire believed that he could correct their calendar. For this reason,
as we have seen, he urged in the last years of his life that his superiors
at Rome send him a competent astronomer. After Ricci's death his
colleagues, especially Pantoja and De Ursis, were repeatedly invited
by the Chinese to translate European scientific books, which meant,
for all practical purposes, the works of Clavius. Also they were invited
to correct the calendar.

The first serious attempts at these tasks were in 1611–1612. But for
the time being the results amounted to nothing. After a pause, the efforts
were resumed in 1629, and this time successfully. The work was completed by means of the introduction of European astronomy into China.
The enormous mistakes committed by the imperial mathematicians for
the eclipse of June 21, 1629, gave the decisive blow. Two months later

the emperor was officially asked to order the correction of the calendar. On September 11 the monarch give his high approval to the appointment of Dr. Paul Hsü Kuang-ch'i to serve as commissioner for this purpose, with Dr. Leo Li Chih-tsao[1] as assistant. Both men were Christians. They immediately appealed to Schreck and Longobardo, whom we have already met. The latter, however, was more than seventy years old and could not do the work. The former died a few months after receiving the appeal. Their places were then filled by persons who subsequently became famous in the history of Western science in China: James Rho of Milan and Adam Schall von Bell of Constance. Aided by a dozen good Chinese literati, the two missionary-scientists over a period of about seven years published a collection of *Books on Mathematics* in approximately 150 small Chinese volumes. Parallel with this publication proceeded the correction of the calendar. On February 28, 1634, the first calendar made in accordance with European methods was offered to the emperor so that he could command that it be printed and distributed in the provinces. At the same time an astronomical almanac indicating the movements of the planets and the aspects of their positions for all the days of the year was compiled. Schall's work was later continued by Verbiest and other renowned Jesuit scientists.[2]

But let us stop at the events of 1611–1612.

On May 11, 1610, Matthew Ricci died at Peking, breathing his last in the arms of his brother, Sabatino De Ursis. Born at Lecce in 1575, De Ursis joined the Society of Jesus in 1597 at Rome. He sailed for India in 1602, and for Macao a year later. Then, while he was preparing at Macao to embark for the mission in Japan, Valignano died, and De Ursis' fate was changed: his scientific training qualified him for China. He reached Peking probably during the first half of 1607, and he lived with Ricci for the last three years of the life of the great missionary from Macerata. In 1616 the first persecution occurred and De Ursis, abandoning Peking, sought refuge at Macao. There he died on May 3, 1620,[3] a decade after Ricci.

Then, when there was talk in 1611–1612 of translating into Chinese the books brought by the European missionaries and of correcting the calendar, De Ursis was the best qualified man at Peking to do the work. At this time, April 1612, the Visitor to the two sister missions in China and Japan, Francis Pasio of Bologna, arrived at Macao. As was to be expected, he requested of De Ursis a memorandum on this subject, and De Ursis compiled his report at the Northern Capital in August 1612, affixing to it the date September 1.

Unfortunately, however, Pasio passed to a better life two days before, August 30,[4] and De Ursis' memorandum had to go to Father Valentine Carvalho,[5] at that time vice-provincial. The report is interesting because it is the first document in a European language to give a clear and neat idea of the Chinese calendar and of the problems relating to it at the beginning of the seventeenth century. Since it had never been published, and since it can be serviceable as a complement to what has been said in the preceding pages, it seemed to me opportune to make it available here to the public[6] . . . with necessary identifications and illustrations of persons and of facts alluded to.[7]

REPORT OF FATHER SABATINO DE URSIS, S.J., TO FATHER FRANCIS PASIO, S.J., ON THE CHINESE CALENDAR
A short account of the Chinese calendar and its errors, for which correction is desired.

{Introduction: Purposes and Sources of this Essay}

At the beginning of the present month of August, I received a letter from Your Reverence in which, because of the concern in this kingdom of China with correcting the calendar, and because of the king's having given us the task, you asked me to draw up a short treatise on the difficulties and uncertainties one meets. You wished to know what the errors are for which correction is desired, and what the purpose of the Chinese is in this correction. Accordingly, I shall put briefly in writing as much as I have read in the *Ephemerides*[8] of the Chinese and what I have learned from our Dr. Paul Hsü Kuang-ch'i[9] and from the royal mathematicians on this subject, even though, because of lack of time, I shall not be able to do justice to the subject nor to Your Reverence's wishes.

Since it is suitable to know something about the origin and order of this calendar of the Chinese, I shall summarize for you some points on its origin; then I shall discuss the order and method which the Chinese follow in it, and finally the errors which now they wish to correct.

{*Origin of the Calendar*}

According to the *Histories,* the Chinese have already used the calendar for 3970 years, which means that they have calculated eclipses, have known the movements of the celestial bodies, and have made other observations, of which I shall say more later. This goes back to the time of a king named Yao 堯. In those days in the kingdom there were two brothers who understood astronomy: Hsi 羲 and Ho 和. Yao commanded them to draw up the rules of the movements of the celestial bodies.[10]

{*The Burning* (213 B.C.) *and Recovery* (145–135 B.C.) *of the Books*}

Two thousand years afterward there was a king of the Ch'in 秦 Dynasty named Shih Huang 始皇 who in the thirty-fourth year of his empire {=213 B.C.} commanded that all books be burned. He forbade anybody to study. He made no exceptions save for books on medicine, divination, sowing, and planting of trees, and a few other books of slight importance.[11] In this fire, which the Chinese still regret, they lost the above-mentioned rules of the calendar. Although they continued to make calculations, they did so, it is said, by oral tradition, and this practice lasted for about 120 years. At the end of this period a king named Wu 武帝 {140–87 B.C.} diligently ordered that the books be sought for in places where according to rumor people had hidden them at the time of the universal burning. Thus, almost all the books were recovered, some from walls where they had been hidden, others from boxes in which they had been buried.[12] Among the findings were the calendar and its rules. Thereafter the use of these rules and books was resumed.

{*Astrology and the Calendar: The Two Observatories*}

For the Chinese there exist two branches of mathematics of which the first is called *t'ien-wên* 天文 and the second *li-fa* 歷法. *T'ien-wên*, strictly speaking, is what we call fortunetelling. *Li-fa* has to do with the calendar and the movements of the celestial bodies theoretically and practically.

T'ien-wên or fortunetelling is prohibited by Chinese law so that save for the mathematicians of the Royal College to whom it appertains officially nobody can study it. *Li-fa* or astronomy, in our sense of the word, is not prohibited and may be studied by anybody.[13] In fact, Dr. Paul Hsü Kuang-ch'i, Dr. Li Chih-tsao,[14] and others of this kingdom have studied it and have even written books on it.

But since mathematics is commonly called *t'ien-wên* among the Chinese, the general idea is that it is prohibited and that nobody may study it. But even so, the fact remains that the kings founded a bureau or special college for this science, and that its members have no other duty than to calculate eclipses, to make the calendar each year, and to observe the stars, the comets, and other prodigious phenomena of the sky, daily and nightly, for the purpose of advising the king and of declaring whether these are good or evil omens.[15] For others besides the official members of this bureau or college to do this work is prohibited under grave sanctions—I mean for them to do the work publicly so that all may know, because privately many who are not members actually do the work.

There are only two colleges of these mathematicians in all China: one in this city of Peking, the other in Nanking. The members are honored mandarins who live on the treasury and whose positions are inherited by their sons. The sons, however, are admitted to succession only after an examination.

{Origin of the Calendar of the Ming Dynasty}

The rules followed by this college for the computation of eclipses and compilation of the calendar had already been corrected 55 times,[16] according to the *Histories*, that is if we assume that the same rules were used in antiquity. The last correction was made 300 years ago [that is, 300 years before 1612] during the lifetime of a famous mathematician named Kuo Shou-ching 郭守敬[17] under the Tartar Dynasty and reign of a Tartar Yüan.[18] Besides this true Chinese calendar 授時歷 to which much importance is attached, there is also the Mohammedan calendar 大統歷 translated 230 years ago, at the time of Hung Wu 洪武,[19] who drove the Tartar kings out of China and from being a cook in a Buddhist monastery became king of China and initiated the reigning dynasty in this country.

Here is the origin of the calendar. In the days of Kuo Shou-ching there came from Persia some Mohammedans who offered the king many books on the theory and practice of the planets. Kuo Shou-ching was unwilling to use the books, so they remained untranslated. The king, however, accepted them and kept them in the royal palace. Then when Hung Wu succeeded to the throne, discovering these books in his palace and being a bibliophile, and, moreover, being desirous of correcting the calendar, he ordered two academicians 翰林院[20] and some Mohammedans who were in China at the time to translate them. This was in the fifteenth year of his reign { =1382}. The academicians were literary mandarins of the same royal college to which our Dr. Paul Hsü Kuang-ch'i now belongs.

{Lack of Theory and of Mathematical Books}

Since, however, those who had come from Persia to offer these books had made their journey almost 70 years before and were no longer in China, only the practical part of their doctrine of the planets was translated. The theoretical part and the other books on mathematics were ignored, though still kept in the royal palace. Thus, the Chinese lack works on mathematics, whether treating of planetary theory or of other scientific or speculative subjects in our European sense. They lack such treatises whether of native or of Mohammedan origin. Hence, even the members of the royal college of mathematicians do not know how to do anything except predict eclipses, tell fortunes, and point out propitious and unpropitious places for building, burying, and the like.

{*Desire for the Theory of the Westerners*}

Therefore, when they saw so many of our books treating of things in a scientific manner, such as the first six *Books of Euclid*,[21] translated by Dr. Paul and Father Matthew Ricci, of happy memory, they wanted them for themselves, because they are talented and love science. This is why they insisted that we continue the translations. Since, however, a work of such importance could not be done on private initiative because of the labor involved and the expenses incurred, arrangements were made to have it done as a work of official character, under order of the king. This had been the case with the Mohammedan books mentioned above.

{*Errors in the Calculation of the Eclipse for December 15, 1610*}

Thus affairs stood at the end of 1610, when the royal mathematicians themselves wanted to propose to the king that he give the order and state the procedure to complete the translation of these books. For the time being there was no question of correcting the calendar. This latter was a work of major importance for China and other inducements were necessary before it could be proposed to the king.

Since, however, the royal mathematicians made a mistake in the eclipse for December 15 of the above-mentioned year, a grave mandarin immediately memorialized the king that the mathematicians should be punished. They had erred by six quarters of an hour in their prediction of the eclipse. If this mistake came from errors in their rules, the king should give the order and state the procedure to correct the rules, because the matter was of importance for the whole kingdom.[22]

The king expedited this memorial and entrusted the affair to the

Ministry of Rites, to which the college of mathematicians is subordinate. The latter then put aside temporarily the translation of our books and began to defend itself by again memorializing the king. Actually it had erred by only a half hour. This memorial was also expedited by the king, who committed the affair to the same Ministry. The Ministry held a consultation and decided that the correction was necessary.

{*The Correction of the Calendar is Decided Upon*}

Informed by the royal mathematicians of our books, and of the possibility of having our aid for this correction, these ministers, therefore, memorialized the king saying that it was necessary to correct the calendar and that the command should be issued that men from all parts of the world should be sought who could accomplish the task. They said also that according to the mathematicians of the royal college the fathers from the Far West had books not possessed by the Chinese, although the college needed them. Also the fathers had various clocks and other instruments not possessed by the Chinese. For this reason the ministers desired that the order be issued to translate these books under the auspices of the college, and that permission be granted to the fathers to help correct the calendar.[23]

This memorial was immediately expedited by the king, who said that his will was for the thing to be done. Accordingly, he commissioned the same Ministry of Rites, to which the responsibility properly belongs, to do it.

{*Establishment of a Bureau of European Astronomy*}

This Ministry, after it had received this commission, immediately began to discuss the method of putting it into execution. It decided finally that two grave mandarins of the kingdom, famous mathematicians,[24] should do the work, and that Doctors Paul and Leo should collaborate with the fathers in translating our books and correcting the calendar.

But this second memorial has not yet been expedited by the king. According to rumor, the reason is that in the same memorial a promotion was requested for the two mandarins who were to do the work. This the king has long been unwilling to grant, even though the mandarins have a right to it. They have been awaiting the king's will to enter their bureau for five or six years. This is why our work has not yet started. The Ministry and the royal mathematicians think of proposing the matter anew to the king in another way.

While we await the expediting of the memorial, we shall start the translation of the books and, with the aid of the books, the reform of the calendar. Although, in fact, the books of the Mohammedans were translated in the past, the rules of the Chinese calendar proper were, nevertheless, not corrected. But the king established a special college where the books of the Mohammedans were available for calculating eclipses, a college which still exists. In it the Mohammedan mandarins compute eclipses and do all the rest in accordance with the already translated books.

This summary is as much as I thought appropriate to write to Your Reverence.

Now I shall add some details about the Chinese calendar.

The Chinese Year

The Chinese, like the Hebrews, use the lunar year. Combining the sun's and moon's movements and introducing intercalary months, they make the lunar year agree as closely as possible with the sun's annual movement. Thus, the ordinary year consists of 12 months, while the intercalary year, twice in 5 years, consists of 13 months. Since the Chinese compute these movements anew every year and bring them into agreement with each other, they do not have the difficulty when they correct their calendar of bringing the lunations or the lunar cycle of 19 years into agreement with the days of the solar year. Nor do they have other difficulties of the practices of the Egyptians and Arabs. In fact, the Chinese insert an anticipatory 1 hour and 28 minutes in their annual calculation, conformably to the Alphonsine reckoning, whereby the new moon falls under the European Golden Number.

In order better to understand this and what follows, it is necessary to know that the Chinese do not have, nor do they seek to have, a perpetual calendar. Every year they draw up a new calendar day by day; then they print it and distribute it throughout the kingdom. The expense of the printing is charged to the king. Even though it amounts to thousands of *taels* 兩[25] they think this sum well employed. For no purpose do they wish a perpetual calendar.

Month, Day, and Hour

The lunar month consists of 29 days, 12 hours, and 44 minutes. The Chinese, therefore, have a great month 大月, as they call it, of 30 days, and a small month 小月 of 29 days. They use the natural day, which is from midnight to midnight. They divide it into 12 equal hours giving to each hour 8 quarters and a few minutes. Thus, they do not divide the natural day into 96 quarters of an hour, as the Europeans do, but into 100. This explains why our hours do not correspond exactly to the Chinese hours. They give a fixed determination to 12 o'clock and 6 o'clock in night and day. Then they divide each quarter of an hour into 100 minutes, each minute into 100 seconds, and so forth, for the rest.

Here is what is desired on this point. Given that the Chinese divide day and night into 100 quarters and the Europeans into 96, to find the correspondence between the quarters and the minutes of the Chinese hours, and the quarters and the minutes of the European hours, from 12 o'clock to 6 o'clock; and to see which anticipates the other, and by how much. In this manner we shall be better able to combine the hours and minutes in the calculation of celestial movements.

{The Three Beginnings of the Year}

This is the way the Chinese determine the beginning of the year. Around the north pole they imagine a great circle similar to what we call *semper apparens*. This circle they divide into 12 parts, or 12 hours, which to render immobile they place always at the same point. Twelve o'clock noon is at the upper part of the circle, 12 midnight at the lower part, 6 A.M. on the west, 6 P.M. on the east, and the other hours can be deduced accordingly.[26]

Among the hours of this clock three are noteworthy: the first, *tzŭ* 子, corresponding to midnight; the second, *ch'ou* 丑, corresponding to 2 A.M.; and the third, *yin* 寅, corresponding to 4 A.M.[27]

These hours have given the Chinese three different beginnings for the year. Since it was said in the Chou 周 Dynasty that heaven was created at midnight, they observed which month it was when on the first day the stars in the tail of the Great Bear pointed to the hour of midnight at sunset. This month they chose as the beginning of the year. Since, however, it was said in the Shang-Yin 商殷 Dynasty that the earth was created at the hour they call *ch'ou* 丑, that is, 2 A.M., they observed in which month those same stars marked that hour. This month they made the beginning of the year. Finally, because in the Hsia 夏 Dynasty, and again now [1612], man was said to have been created at the hour *yin* 寅, that is, 4 A.M., they observed in which month the stars in the tail of the Great Bear marked 4 A.M. at sunset. This month they made the beginning of the year.[28] Thus, those who compile the calendar each year put two characters on the first day of each month, one of which indicates the year, the other the hour; and the month is said to start at this hour. But on the first day of the year, each year, the calendar makers affix the character *yin* 寅, that is, 4 A.M.

The month with which the year at the present time [1612] begins corresponds to February for the following reason. They have a sign of the zodiac which they call *li-ch'un* 立春, meaning the beginning of spring. It occurs a month and a half before the vernal equinox and corresponds to February 5. Now the first new moon nearest to this sign is taken as the first month of the year.[29]

What seems to be needed in this is to know right now, at this time of February 5, at what position in the heavens the above-named stars are at sunset. However, even if they were not at that given point, the Chinese would not for this reason be disposed to change their method of initiating the year.

Epact and Golden Number

Since the Chinese draw up the calendar year by year, and calculate the movements of the planets day by day, they have no epact. The difficulty coming from the epact, therefore, does not occur in the correction which they wish to make. The same may be said for the Golden Number.

They have, however, characters analogous to the Golden Number. So I shall speak briefly of these. The Chinese possess 12 characters (the "celestial trunks" 天干) which they call year characters 歲陰, and 12 others (the "terrestrial branches" 地支) which they call the 12 horary characters 十二時. Indeed, they do not count hours as the Europeans do, saying 1, 2, 3, and so forth. Each hour has its own proper character.[30]

Now these characters are combined in this manner: the first year character is joined to the first horary character, and these 2 characters indicate the first year of a total of 60, since 60 different combinations exhaust the possibilities of combining the 10 year characters with the 12 horary characters. Thus, one has, as it were, a century of 60 years. The series then is started over again from the first combination, continuing always in the same way.[31] One would suppose it very difficult to know a past year. Nevertheless, for them it is simple because they know in what order these centuries come, knowing the time of the reign of the kings.[32]

They use these combinations to indicate not only the years but also the days of the year, naming the first day of the month by the first binomial, and thus for the rest. When they have completed the cycle they recommence it, as we said in the case of the years. They also use these combinations of characters for the hours, assigning a combination to each hour. The use of these combined characters is, then, great. We shall see later some of the mysteries contained in them.[33]

The Solar Cycle and the Dominical Letter

Although the Chinese do not have this cycle or the dominical letter, we can repeat on this subject what we have already said about the Golden Number, since they have analogous things in their calendar.

The Chinese have 28 constellations. Each possesses a proper name consisting of one character. To each constellation corresponds a planet, and since there are 7 planets, each planet corresponds to 4 of these constellations. This is really equivalent to the number 28 to our solar cycle. Since they apply one of these characters of the constellations to each day of the week, the 4 constellations corresponding to the sun always fall on Sunday, those corresponding to the moon always fall on Monday, those corresponding to Mars on Tuesday, and so forth. And this always happens thus.[34] In fact, given that there is no interruption by a bissextile year, that the constellations are divided into 4 groups, and that at the end of the number 28 one begins over again with the first constellation, since the days of the week are necessarily 7, the same 4 constellations recur always the same day. The names of the constellations corresponding to the planet of the sun are: *hsing* 星, *fang* 房, *hsü* 虚, and *mao* 昴.[35]

Because these characters occur day after day in the Chinese calendar, Christians can keep count with it of Sundays and hence of the other days of the week by observing to which days the sun corresponds. This Christians now use, though it is valid only for Sundays. Feast-days, indeed, are printed without Sundays. Christians thus, looking at the calendar, know that the day under which there is one of these four characters is a Sunday.

Since then the Chinese, as we have said above, every year make a new calendar, in the correction of this they do not know the difficulties pointed out here, as was the case with the correction of the Gregorian calendar, in which almost all the difficulty had to do with these matters.

Some Peculiarities of the Chinese Calendar

Besides the above-mentioned things which seem to resemble our calendar slightly, the Chinese have in their calendar, day by day, other things similar to our prognostications, as used to be done in Europe, although there are great differences. Indeed, these Chinese things cannot have any cause, yet they are believed in so much that they infallibly are observed.[36]

The things which they say one can or cannot do on this or that day are as follows. They say, for example: today one can sacrifice, today the king can make payments and concede benefits, one can cure sicknesses, let blood, invite to dinner, take a bath, take a trip, move, remove earth, build, raise columns or beams for the roofs of houses, plant trees, invite people home, start a study, dig a well, break a seal, and similar things. They do not do all these things the same day, but on one day, one, two, or three, and another day, none. Thus, to do such and such a thing, they necessarily await that day, otherwise the thing would not succeed nor would they find the luck which they say would be obtained if it were done on such and such a fixed day and hour of the calendar.

Although, as I have said, these observations do not depend on any cause, I shall describe the method by which they arrive at them.

First of all, since they believe that to each of the 10 year characters mentioned above[37] one of their 5 elements[38] corresponds, it follows that each of these year characters has the property of the element corresponding to it. The same may be said for the 12 horary characters. Moreover, each of the 60 combinations of the characters in these two series has its proper element. Besides this, one of the 7 planets corresponds to each of the 7 groups of 4 constellations into which the 28 constellations fall. Now, in the calendar the combinations of characters from the two series are inserted daily to indicate the day, and under each particular combination, on each day, the constellation is inserted which falls on that day. Since the combinations of characters from the two series signify elements, and since the constellations indicate planets, they, studying the properties of the element predominating on a given day, and the properties of the planet governing that day, deduce whether the day is auspicious or inauspicious. It is true that other observations having to do with these properties also enter into the matter, for which reason the Chinese have written many books on the subject. But it finally all reduces to what I have said. This is the basis for the Chinese art of fortunetelling and for all their other divinatory practices.

In addition, the calendar contains under the first day of each month notations of the hour and quarter-hour of the new moon, the hours of the quarters of the moon and of the full moon. Also there are indications of the day, hour, and quarter-hour of the equinoxes and solstices, with the day, hour, and quarter-hour in which the sun enters the other signs. The length of the day and night is given for the first day in which the sun enters a sign, with the hour and quarter-hour of the sun's rising and setting. Finally, the degree of the planets' positions is noted for each day.

Thus ends the calendar.

The Zodiac and the Division of Degrees According to the Chinese

The Chinese know the equinoctial line and the zodiac but their books do not speak of the properties or use of these. They say only that the sun always travels along the middle of the zodiac and that the moon follows nine ways 九道, according to whether it leaves or enters the ecliptic and according to whether its direction is one or another of the four cardinal points: north, south, east, and west.[39] They give to each of these nine ways a name. They divide these ways so well that they form 363 consecutive places according to the positions at which eclipses can occur. This arrangement is useful to them in their calculations.

They make no mention of the division of the equinoctial line. They only divide the zodiac into 365 degrees and 24 minutes, exactly as many as there are days in the solar year. They distribute these degrees in equal parts among the 24 signs, each sign being allotsed 15 days, 21 quarters, and 84 minutes. Since they do not know the culmination, the eccentrics, or the concentrics of the sun, which cause its unequal motion in the zodiac, they cannot distribute the signs as the Europeans do. We Europeans, because of this unequal motion, distribute the days through the 30-degree intervals of the zodiac of the *primum mobile,* even this unequally. Consequently, their signs cannot agree with the European signs, nor is there correspondence as to the days when the sun enters them, save for the two equinoxes and the two solstices. In these latter cases the difference is by the quantity of the errors of movements to be corrected.

In the division of degrees they follow the centesimal system, so that they divide the degree into 100 minutes, the minute into 100 seconds, the second into 100 thirds, and so forth, down to the tenth, in the same manner as we divide to the tenth part. Thus, for the number of degrees and minutes of the planets, and for other celestial movements, there can be no correspondence with the European figures.

The Heavens and Their Movements According to the Chinese

Although the Chinese ordinarily say that there are nine heavens 九重, they do not speak of them in their *Ephemerides,* nor do they speak of eccentrics, concentrics, or epicycles. They have no knowledge of the proper motion of the planets from west to east, nor of other ob-servations which the Europeans make.[40] In particular, they have no knowledge of parallax or differences of aspect so necessary in as-tronomy.

But here is what they know. They determine a general or imaginary movement representing the space to be traversed from one winter solstice to another solstice according to their rules. They follow the movement through this space. It corresponds to the "date of the year" of the Europeans.

Since they divide the day into 100 quarters, and the quarter into 100 minutes, so that a day has 10,000 minutes, they say that the movement mentioned above is of 3,652,575 minutes. For the Chinese the motions of the planets are fixed. Thus, they follow the planets according to the movement mentioned above. They attribute to the sun a motion of 3,652,425 minutes. Hitherto, they have made their calculations, as I have described, without knowing whether the motions of the planets are in the same heaven or in different heavens, in spite of the fact that the motions of the planets are so different from the quantity of the year.

They say nothing about the cause of retardations and accelerations. Nor do they speak of the other properties of the planets. Indeed, as we have mentioned above, the only books they possess are the tables for calculating eclipses and the movements of the planets.

Method Followed by the Chinese in the Correction of Their Calendar

Since the Chinese have no planetary theory but only the tables of which we have spoken, they cannot scientifically correct the errors in the movements of the planets in which consists the correction of their calendar. They do it, however, in practice taking only the shadow of the sun by which they easily find the solstice, which is that of winter, whence they begin their observations as the Europeans begin theirs with the spring equinox. Here is how they do it.

They take a rod eight arms high. They divide it into degrees and minutes. Then three days before and three days after the winter solstice they observe the shadow every day and note its degrees and minutes. From these two measures of the shadow they deduce very well within these six days the day, hour, and quarter in which the solstice occurred. They repeat this in various parts of the kingdom for three or four solstices. They spend much time at this, which is the occupation of the greater mandarins of the court. In this consists the principal part of this correction.

The rest of their time they devote to adjusting the movements of the planets in accordance with their correction of the date of the year. With this aim they observe stars at night on a mountain where they have the needful instruments. According to their *Histories,* fifty-five corrections have been made up until now. The last was done three hundred years ago at the time of the aforementioned Kuo Shou-ching,[41] who not only determined the winter solstice, but also the altitudes of places, of which the Chinese have very little knowledge. Since this happened at the time of the Yüan, the Tartar kings, it is said that he went 67 degrees from the Tartars and 19 degrees to the south; but he went also east and west, in which he spent 16 years.

If the Chinese attach so much importance to this correction and if the greatest of the court are occupied with it, it is because in their calendar they indicate the things which one ought to do on such and such a day and at such and such an hour, especially in regard to the dead, a very important matter in China. They say that if there is an error in the day and hour of the winter solstice, all the days of the year will be wrong, because one says that it is such and such a day when it is not; and if the conjunction of the moon is mistaken, equally also the days and the hours are mistaken. In such a case the whole kingdom is deceived by its great prejudice because people do not do the things on the day and at the hour when they would find the luck which they ought to have.

Errors to be Corrected in the Chinese Calendar

Since the Chinese do not have in their calendar epact, Golden Number, solar cycle, or other things which we have in our Gregorian calendar, as was said above,[42] the difficulty of correcting their calendar centers on two matters only: first, *sui-ch'a* 歲差, meaning annual error, which is exactly what we call precession of the equinoxes; second, the true movement of the planets, so that eclipses of the sun and moon can be well calculated.

The Chinese knowledge of the precession of the equinoxes does not come from knowledge that the eighth sphere moves *motu trepidationis*, or that it has a motion of its own in common with the ninth sphere. Rather it comes only from their having found a difference on the day of the winter solstice. Thus they say that at the time of a king named Han Wu Ti 漢武帝 [140–87 B.C.] they discovered that the sun had varied by 24 degrees from the time of the first king until then, that is, during a period of 2000 years. Speaking of this difference, they attribute it not to the displacement of the stars, but to the displacement of the solstice. The solstice now, therefore, is at such and such a degree in such and such a constellation. Later it will be elsewhere, varying continually. But they assign no reason. Accordingly, a king named I Hsi 義熙[43] commanded that this difference be corrected. Some said that the difference was one degree every 55 years; others gave the interval as every 100 years; others, every 75 years; others, every 83 years. Finally, the above-mentioned mathematician[44] established that it happened every 66 years. This they still believe.

In this matter we have no difficulty because Dr. Paul Hsü Kuang-ch'i has seen our precession of the equinoxes as explained by Father Clavius and Anthony Magini in their theory. He finds the matter very reasonable and he avoids the errors made by all other mathematicians of China. Nevertheless, one of the prime desiderata has to do with this subject of precession.

The Chinese also know the movements of the planets. But besides lacking the above-mentioned precession of the equinoxes their tables of these movements are mistaken. Hence, in their computation of eclipses they ordinarily err by three or four quarters. This error is not attributable to parallax or diversity of aspect alone, because in eclipses at noon, when these differences do not occur, an error of one hour equally remains. Their books, as we have said,[45] take no account of this. Yet the following paragraph occurs among the rules of their tables: "If the solar eclipse is before noon, the number must be subtracted; if it is after noon, the number must be added." But this is all. If then anybody should ask the mathematicians why, they would not know the answer. They would only say that they have the tables for executing the calculations but that they do not know what the calculations themselves are.

Your Reverence, thus, can already see that the whole difficulty of correcting the calendar consists in this: to find the true movements of all the celestial bodies, to make tables for calculating eclipses, and to prepare everything needful to this end, as Your Reverence knows well.

I shall add, however, that the intention of Dr. Paul is not to correct their tables by means of ours, but to take ours as they are and to do with us as they did with the Mohammedans. Indeed, dividing degrees and minutes in the way mentioned above, they find the greatest difficulty not only in the use of their distribution but also in the correction made with our sexagesimal division; this pleases everybody much and succeeds easily, as, in fact, it is [easy].

So much for the correction of the calendar.

{*Scientific Books to be Translated and Instruments to be Procured*}

Although the foregoing is very important, the chief intention of the royal mathematicians is to translate some of our books which they do not have in their college; also to have clocks, instruments for measuring stars, elevations, and so forth, and other useful instruments such as hydraulic devices, devices for lifting weights, leveling water, restoring rivers, drying up marshes and lagoons, which exist in great abundance in this kingdom, and other instruments which they know exist in large number in the Great Occident—to use their expression.

All this prepares souls well for the goal which our Society has in this kingdom. In this way, we gain credit among the literati, who are disposed to be satisfied with what they have, and to believe that nobody can teach them anything. It is good for them to be in this frame of mind. Even the common people dislike foreigners and have a special manner toward them. So these things by which we arouse their affection and benevolence toward us are necessary at the beginning of our apostolate, because of the fruit coming therefrom, until our Lord opens wider the gates for the preaching of the Gospel.

Longitude of the City of Peking

One of the essentials for correcting the calendar is to know the longitude of this city. Therefore it will be necessary to observe eclipses. This still has not been done with exactitude. Nevertheless, I shall tell here what has been done with the eclipses of the current year, 1612, from which the longitude is deducible.

Here is how the eclipse of the moon which occurred May 15 was observed. We were up on a very high tower. Since the eclipse took place toward morning, it was easy to observe it with the sand hourglass, so that when the eclipse had barely begun one turned to the hourglass. We remained up on the tower until the sun rose above the horizon. Thus, we found that three quarters and a half passed. Because on May 15 the sun rises at four and three-quarters and a half, the eclipse accordingly started at four in the morning, though in my opinion it started at five minutes after four. Now in Lisbon it was said that the eclipse would take place on May 14 at sixteen minutes after six in the evening. Granted that the calculation of the eclipse was exact, the difference between these two cities would be nine hours and one minute, which equals 135°.[46] If we add 5°10′ representing the distance between Lisbon and the Fortunate Isles, we get 140° plus, which is the longitude of this city.

The mathematicians of the royal college erred with this eclipse of the moon by almost three quarters. For this reason a memorial against them was presented to the king, and he deprived them of three months' salary. They also said that an eclipse of the sun was to occur on May 30 at six and three-quarters. This was not verified although there were no clouds. The college of Mohammedans which, as was said,[47] is in this court, said that there would be no eclipse, as in fact happened.

{*Prediction of Eclipses for the Years 1613–1615*}

In the Chinese calendar which they make year by year, although there are all those things which we have mentioned, still there are no eclipses, because these are not announced in advance. Instead the king is informed two or three months ahead that an eclipse will occur on such and such a day and at such and such an hour. He then issues orders that the whole kingdom be notified so that on that day everybody will be ready to perform ceremonies. Although this is the state of affairs they still calculate eclipses according to the rules of the Chinese college proper.

In order, therefore, that proceedings may be facilitated for the determination of the longitude of this city I shall indicate here some future eclipses.

In 1613 on the fifteenth of the third month there will be an eclipse of the moon of thirteen minutes, which will begin at five and three-quarters, and so forth, in the evening; the third month corresponds to the end of April, and so forth. On the fifteenth of the ninth month of the same year, that is, at the end of October, there will be another eclipse of the moon of fifteen minutes, which will begin at nine plus in the evening.

In 1614 on the fifteenth of the new moon there will be an eclipse of the moon of four points and it will begin at ten and one-quarter in the evening, and so forth.

In 1615 on the first of the third moon there will be an eclipse of the sun of nine points, which will begin at three and one-quarter after noon, and so forth.

Thus much have I been able to write summarily to Your Reverence about the Chinese calendar and its correction. Your Reverence sees, thus, without difficulty, how easy this correction is, since in Europe very exact tables exist for calculating eclipses. Even among us, in fact, there is a great variety.

To calculate an eclipse of the sun the Chinese use three months, according to what a royal mathematician has told me. Therefore, we have not yet told the mandarins the time and hour of the [above-mentioned] eclipses, although they have been asked about them. We have in fact always replied that since it was necessary to use so much time it has not yet been possible to make the calculation. Rather, since they have established that nine years are necessary, they are persuaded that after nine years, when everything has been finished and the true longitude and altitude of places have been determined, which they wished to be done last year, we shall tell them the time and the hour of the eclipses. In such manner, praise be to Our Lord, we have time for everything and for Your Reverence to arrange for what we most need for the mission.

Herewith and requesting your holy benediction I commend myself to Your Reverence's prayers.

Peking, September 1, 1612.

Your Reverence's son in Christ,
SABATINO DE URSIS

NOTES

1. *Echi delle scoperte Galileiane in Cina.*
2. *Galileo e la Compagnia di Gesù. Dal Collegio Romano all'Estremo Oriente.*
3. *Sidereus Nuncius.*
4. *Studi Galileiani.*
5. *Echi delle scoperte Galileiane in Cina vivente ancora Galileo* (1612–1640), in *Atti della Accademia Nazionale dei Lincei*, series VIII, *Rendiconti*, Class of Moral, Historical, and Philological Sciences (Rome, 1946), vol. I, pp. 125–193.
6. [*Galileo in Cina. Relazioni attraverso il Collegio Romano tra Galileo e i gesuiti scienziati missionari in Cina* (1610–1640) (Rome, 1947), in *Analecta Gregoriana, cura Pontificiae Universitatis Gregorianae edita*, vol. XXXVII, series Facultatis Missiologicae, section A (n. 1). By Pasquale M. D'Elia, S. J., "professore di Sinologia nella Pontificia Università Gregoriana e nella Università degli Studi di Roma." This is the work of which the present volume is an English translation.]

INTRODUCTION, CHAPTERS 1–30 AND EPILOGUE

1. The following abbreviations are used in this study: APGU, Archives of the Pontifical Gregorian University (Archivio della Pontificia Università Gregoriana); D'Elia, *Fonti Ricciane*, vol. I, *Storia dell'Introduzione del Cristianesimo in Cina*, part I, 1582–1597 (Rome, 1942) and vol. II, *Storia dell'Introduzione del Cristianesimo in Cina*, part II, 1597–1611 (Rome, 1949), and vol. III, *Storia dell'-Introduzione del Cristianesimo in Cina*, appendices and indices (Rome, 1949); Fang Hao, *Fang Hao Wên lu* 方豪文錄: *Studies in the History of the Relations between China and the West* by Rev. Maur Fang Hao (Peiping, Institutum Sancti Thomae, 1948). Gabrieli, *Il Carteggio Linceo della vecchia Accademia di Federico Cesi* (1603–1630) (Rome, 1938–1941); Galilei, *Edizione Nazionale delle Opere di Galileo Galilei* (Florence); RASJ, Roman Archives of the Society of Jesus (Archivio Romano della Compagnia di Gesù); Tacchi Venturi, *Opere Storiche del P. Matteo Ricci*, II (Macerata, 1913). The Fang Hao work is a valuable collection of thirty-nine different articles which Rev. Don Maur Fang Hao of the secular clergy has written in several Chinese dailies or reviews shortly before or shortly after 1940. All the articles are in Chinese; only the general title of the collection and the titles of the articles are, besides being in Chinese, also in English. In this collection two articles refer to the subject of this book: "Galileo and the Introduction of Science into China" (pp. 287–292) and "Introduction of the Telescope into China, Corea and Japan before the Death of Galileo" (pp. 292–294).

2. The Chinese sources, in Rome, are to be found in the Roman Archives of the Society of Jesus, and in the Vatican Library.

3. [This refers, of course, to the Italian translation.]

4. Cathay was already marked on planispheres and geographical charts of the early fourteenth century, for example, the globe of Fra Paolino, those of Peter Visconte, and derivative works. Compare R. Almagià, *Monumenta cartographica Vaticana*, vol. I (Vatican City, 1944), plates I, V, X. Cambaluc, under the name *chanbalech*, appears in a showy manner on the celebrated Catalan map, Paris, 1375, and on other maps of the fourteenth century. Compare Nordenskjöld, *Periplus* (Stockholm, 1897), plate XIV; and Hållberg, J., *L'Extrême Orient dans la Littérature et dans la cartographie de l'Occident des XIII, XIV et XV siècles* (Göteborg, 1907), under the respective words. I owe this note Professor R. Almagià.

to5. See D'Elia, I, p. 139, n. 5.

6. *Ibid.*, p. 207, n. 3.

7. *Ibid.*, p. 143, n. 2.

8. For Matthew Ricci see the National Edition of his works, edited by me with ample commentary, under the title *Fonti Ricciane* (3 vols.; Rome, Libreria dello Stato, 1942, 1949). For the earliest efforts to introduce European astronomy into China during the seventeenth century see also my study, *Il contributo dei missionari cattolici alla scambievole conoscenza della Cina e dell'Europa*, in *Le Missioni Cattoliche e la Cultura dell'Oriente* (Rome, 1943), pp. 27-109.

9. He means astronomy.

10. That is, the calendar. See D'Elia, I, n. 417.

11. See Tacchi Venturi, II, p. 285.

12. In the sense of astronomer.

13. See D'Elia, II, n. 504. See also *ibid.*, I, n. 417.

14. See Tacchi Venturi, II, pp. 284-285.

15. See *ibid.*, p. 343.

16. "En particular desseava el Padre Cattaneo (y es desseo de los más Padres de la missión) hun buen matematico . . . Y de la matematica me escrivió el Padre Matheos Riçio le tenía aiudado mucho para mostrar a los Chinas la falsidad de algunos sus yerros con que despues hechavan también los otros." See RASJ, *Jap.-Sin.*, 13, f. 358 *v.* ["In particular, Father Cattaneo desired a good mathematician (and it is the desire of most the fathers of the mission) . . . And concerning mathematics, Father Matthew Ricci wrote me that he has had much help from it in showing to the Chinese some of their errors by means of which they afterwards also committed other errors."]

17. See APGU, 530, f. 3r; reproduced in Galilei, X, p. 23.

18. See APGU, 530, f. 4r; reproduced in Galilei, X, p. 27.

19. ["Cannone" means cannon, "occhiale" means eye-piece. Thus the derivation of the Italian word for telescope: "cannocchiale."]

20. The word "telescopio" was invented by John Demisiani, or more probably by Prince Frederick Cesi. See Galilei, XI, p. 420, n. 4. From the Italian

word "cannocchiale" is derived the Chinese word *chien-ni-cha* 諫尼渣, but with
the Cantonese pronunciation, as one reads in the *History of Macao: Ao-mên chi
lüeh* 澳門記略, II, f. 58*b*.

21. To be found in Galilei, III¹, pp. 1–96.

22. See APGU, 530, f. 155*r*; reproduced in Galilei, X, p. 273. [Professor
Donald H. Menzel, in a communication to the translators, points out that according to these figures Galileo evidently thought that the diameter of the earth
was 4000 miles.]

23. Their observations were transmitted to us by Galileo, to whom, evidently, they had been sent. See Galilei, III², pp. 861–864.

24. See Galilei, X, pp. 484–485.

25. See *ibid.*, pp. 499–502.

26. "Certe nisi ipse, saltem eo modo quo per Romana instrumenta licuit,
ea quae recenter et primus in orbem prodigia invexisti, ipse, oculis propris
inspexissem, aliisque nonnullis commonstrassem, nescio si adhuc tuis rationibus
assentirer . . . Iam Clavius, iam quotquot fere Romae nova phenomena in-
spexere, tecum sentiunt, vel minus certe quam antea a te dissentiunt; et ego
sane plurimum mirarer, si quis reperiretur qui ea quae vidi viderit, non vero
crediderit. Talis profecto non tecum, sed secum cumque sensu, volens atque
ex industria pugnaverit" (Galilei, XI, p. 33). [Translation of the Latin has
been substituted here in the text for D'Elia's paraphrase of it. The last sentence,
not translated in the text of the Italian edition, means: "Indeed, such a one
would fight not with you, but voluntarily and deliberately with himself."]

27. See Galilei, X, pp. 479–480.

28. See APGU, 529, f. 73; reproduced in Galilei, X, p. 484.

29. See Galilei, X, p. 288.

30. See *ibid.*, XII, p. 99.

31. This friend was Anthony Santini. See *ibid.*, XI, p. 34.

32. See APGU, 530, f. 183*r*.

33. See APGU, 529, f. 74; reproduced in Galilei, XI, p. 45.

34. See Galilei, XI, p. 120; *ibid.*, p. 132.

35. E. C. Phillips, *The Correspondence of Fr. Christopher Clavius S.J., preserved in the Archives of the Pontifical Gregorian University*, in *Archivum Historicum
Societatis Iesu*, VIII (Rome, 1939), pp. 193–222.

36. See APGU, 530, f. 182*r*.

37. See Galilei, XI, pp. 79–80.

38. See *ibid.*, p. 89.

39. There is now no longer any doubt that Clavius before his death saw the
need of modifying ancient positions by adopting the Copernican system. The
last edition of the five large volumes of his works was printed in 1611, except
for volume V which appeared posthumously in 1612. In this last edition
shortly before his death, he wrote:

"Nolo tamen hoc loco lectorem latere non ita pridem ex Belgio apportatum
esse instrumentum quoddam instar tubi cuiusdam oblongi in cuius basibus

contracta sunt duo vitra seu perspicilla, quo obiecta a nobis remota valde propinqua apparent et quidem longe maiora quam reipsa sunt. Hoc instrumento cernuntur plurimae stellae in firmamento quae sine eo nullo modo videri possunt, praesertim in Pleiadibus, circa Nebulosam Cancri, in Orione, in Via Lactea et alibi . . . Luna quoque, quando est corniculata aut semiplena, mirum in modum refracta et aspera apparet, ut mirari satis non possim in corpore lunari tantas inesse inaequalitates. Verum hac de re consule libellum Galilaei Galilaei, quem Sidereum Nuncium inscripsit, Venetijs impressum anno 1610, in quo varias observationes stellarum a se primo factas describit. Inter alia quae hoc instrumento visuntur, hoc non postremum locum obtinet, nimirum Venerem recipere lumen a sole instar lunae, ita ut corniculata nunc magis nunc minus, pro distantia eius a sole, appareat. Id quod non semel cum alijs hic Romae observavi. Saturnus quoque habet coniunctas duas stellas ipso minores, unam versus orientem et versus occidentem alteram. Iuppiter denique habet quatuor stellas erraticas, quae mirum in modum situm et inter se et cum Iove variant, ut diligenter et accurate Galilaeus Galilaei describit. Quae cum ita sint, videant Astronomi quo pacto orbes coelestes constituendi sint ut haec phaenomena possint salvari." *Opera Mathematica*, vol. III (Mainz, 1611), p. 75. ["I do not wish here, however, to conceal from the reader that a short time ago a certain oblong instrument was brought from Belgium, at the opposite ends of which were assembled two glasses or lenses, by means of which objects remote from us appear near, and certainly much greater than they actually are. By this instrument are discerned many stars in the heavens which without it are invisible, particularly in the Pleiades, in the nebula in Cancer [Praesepe or the Bee-hive], in Orion, in the Milky Way, and elsewhere. . . . The moon, also, when it is horned or half full, appears amazingly broken up and rough, so that I was spellbound at the many inequalities in the lunar body. Concerning this matter, consult Galileo Galilei's little book, *The Sidereal Messenger*, printed at Venice in 1610, in which he describes various observations of stars made by him for the first time. Among other things disclosed by this instrument, not the least important is the evidence that Venus, like the moon, receives its light from the sun, so that it is horned, now more, now less, in accordance with its distance from the sun. I and others have often observed this here at Rome. Saturn also has two smaller stars conjoined with it, one toward the east and the other toward the west. Finally, Jupiter has four small wandering stars which in an amazing, fixed manner move among themselves and in their relation to Jupiter, as Galileo Galilei diligently and accurately describes. Since these things are so, let astronomers see how the celestial spheres must be constituted in order to save these phenomena."]

Galileo himself, in his letter of 1615 to Christine of Lorraine, wrote: "I could name for you other mathematicians who, moved by my late discoveries, admit the need of reconceiving the constitution of the universe, because it is absolutely impossible to stand as it is." In the margin he wrote that one of these was "Clavius" (Galilei, V, p. 328). Even after 1616 and 1633, Clavius and other

Jesuits favored the Copernican system. Nicholas Fabri di Peiresc (see Galilei, XX, p. 504), known as the "procurator-general of letters" for his patronage of literature, in September 1633, wrote to Peter Gassendi about a recent visit of Father Athanasius Kircher to Aix, "[Kircher] ne se peult tenir de nous advoüer en présence du P. {John} Ferrand {S.J.}, que le P. {Charles} Malapertius {Malapert S.J., professor of mathematics, astronomer, 1580–1630} et le P. Clavius mesmes n'improuvoient nullement l'advis de Copernicus, ains ne s'en esloignoient guières, encores qu'on les eusse pressez et obligez d'escrire pour les communes suppositions d'Aristote, que le P. Scheiner mesmes ne suyvoit que par force et par obédiance, aussy bien que luy" (Galilei, XV, p. 254). ["(Kircher) could not help but avow, in the presence of Father { John} Ferrand {S.J.}, that Father {Charles} Malapert {S.J., professor of mathematics and astronomer, 1580–1630} and Father Clavius do not disapprove of the opinion of Copernicus. In fact, they barely differ from it. They are obliged, however, to write in accordance with the common suppositions of Aristotle, which Father Scheiner follows only by force and obedience, as does (Kircher) himself."]

40. Father Van Maelcote, who gave the formal discourse at the convocation in Galileo's honor in May 1611, returned to Flanders the following year, and died in 1615, before the injunction of 1616. Gregory of St. Vincent, another pupil of Clavius and an enthusiastic admirer of Galileo, was not at Rome at the time of this injunction. The only man who could perhaps have said something in favor of the Pisan astronomer was Grienberger, who in 1615 most certainly conferred on the matter with Bellarmine, who at that time was of the opinion that the Holy Office would give Galileo no trouble. Was Grienberger questioned after Galileo's affairs took a turn for the worse? Lack of documentary evidence prevents me from answering this question. It is certain that Grienberger, as will be seen later (n. 50), although not admitting all of Galileo's ideas, inclined towards the Copernican system, as even Scheiner inclined, who was his bitter opponent on other points. For Bellarmine Galileo was, from before April 19, 1611, a "capable mathematician," as he expressed himself in his letter to the mathematicians of the Roman College. He himself at this period had observed with the telescope "some very marvelous things concerning the moon and Venus" (Galilei, XI, p. 87).

41. He was born in the Swiss part of the diocese of Constance. Compare Alfons Väth, S.J., *Johann Adam Schall von Bell S.J.* (Cologne, 1933), p. 85, n. 48; Joh. Beckmann, *Ein Schweizermissionar am Kaiserhof von Peking. P. Johann Terenz S.J.* ("Bethlehem," 1934), pp. 171–173, 221–224.

42. Schreck wrote from Kiating on April 22, 1622: "Dominus Castellus . . . videtur superare illum presbyterum qui nobiscum in monte S. Trinitatis per tubum Galilaei nolebat stellas contemplari, ne cogeretur asserere verum esse quod visus dictitabat" (Gabrieli, *Giovanni Schreck Linceo*, in *Rendiconti* of the Royal National Academy of the Lincei, Class of Moral, Historical, and Philological Studies, series VI, vol. XII (Rome, 1937), p. 504). ["Peter Castelli is seen to excel that 'presbyter' who, when he was with us on the Trinità dei

Monti, was unwilling to look at the stars through Galilei's tube lest he be forced to admit that what he said he saw was true."] Is the word "presbyter" taken here in the etymological sense of old, or in the metaphorical and popular sense of priest, or is it perhaps owed to a lapse of memory on the part of Schreck. I should not know what to say. It is certain that Caesar Cremonino (1550–1631), professor of literature at the University of Padua (Galilei, XX, p. 429) obstinately refused to look through the telescope. See Galilei, XI, pp. 100, 165. If he is the "presbyter" of whom Schreck speaks, the word can only mean old, since Cremonino in 1611 was sixty-one years old while Schreck was thirty-five.

43. *Nuncius Sidereus.*

44. See Galilei, III[1], pp. 291–298.

45. *De Lunarum Montium Altitudine.*

46. See Galilei, XI, pp. 233, 273; XX, p. 545.

47. "Reverentia Vestra, quaeso, haec bono animo dicta boni consulat et si fieri possit, Dominum Galileum, ut decet, mathematicum tradat. Scio non omnia quae dicit esse de fide, sed video etiam ex altera parte, non essent adeo absurda ut non potius excusari debeat quam publice reprehendi" (APGU, 534, f. 87r).

48. For Father Biancani's reply and Galileo's letter see *Edizione Completa delle Opere di Galileo Galilei*, Bologna, II, pp. 102–123. Both documents are reproduced in Galilei, XI, pp. 126–127, 178–203.

49. See Galilei, XI, p. 233; see *ibid.*, p. 273.

50. Grienberger's sympathy must be read between the lines rather than actually proved. After Father Scheiner's first publication on the sunspots, written under the pseudonym Apelles, Faber wrote to Galileo on November 23, 1612, that Grienberger had visited eight days before. "He knows well," said Faber, "that {Apelles} is a Jesuit. But he agrees with Your Lordship more than with Apelles, since he regards Your Lordship's arguments that the sunspots are not stars as sound" (Galilei, XI, p. 434). The scriptural arguments against Copernicus did not, of course, leave Grienberger cold, as is to be expected of a priest in those days. Accordingly, on March 7, 1615, a friend warned Galileo: "The aforementioned father {Grienberger} suspects that your arguments may be more plausible than true, since a certain other passage of Scripture casts doubt upon them" (Galilei, XII, pp. 151–152). In this same year, however, Grienberger wrote to the Bohemian Jesuit, Kirwitzer, as will be seen below, expressing approval of the Copernican system. Also in 1615, Bellarmine, still believing that Galileo had nothing to fear from the authorities, indicated that he would discuss these matters with Grienberger. It is not to be wondered at, therefore, that when the injunction of 1616 came Grienberger and another professor at the Roman College, as well as Schreck, were grieved. Thus, shortly after the handing down of the decree, Prince Cesi wrote to Galileo (October 8, 1616): "Father Grienberger and Father Gulden visited me many days ago and they show affection for Your Lordship and displeasure at the

recent negotiations, especially Father Gulden" (Galilei, XII, p. 285). Indeed, Grienberger's sympathy for Galileo was so clear, at least to Cesi, that the nobleman wanted Galileo to dedicate his *Saggiatore* [*The Assayer*], in answer to Father Grassi, to him. The only reason that this was not done was to avoid "embarrassing that poor father {Grienberger}, a fortunate decision in view of what followed" (Galilei, XIII, p. 44). Even after the sentence of 1633, Grienberger kept his sympathy for Galileo, although he did not adhere to what the Holy Office condemned. Shortly before the sentence, Evangelista Torricelli wrote to Galileo, September 11, 1632: "My friend, Father Grienberger, confesses that Your Lordship's book {*Dialogo sopra i due massimi sistemi del mondo* [*Dialogue Concerning the Two Principal Systems of the World*]} gives him the keenest delight. He thinks that there are many fine things in it, but he does not commend your opinion [of the motion of the earth]. He regards it as plausible only, and not as true" (Galilei, XIV, p. 387). In view of such evidence we must conclude, therefore, that the unnamed friend who reported to Galileo a rather vindictive remark allegedly made by Grienberger was merely a malicious talebearer. This friend reported that during a conversation in early 1634 he heard Grienberger say: "Galileo should have known how to keep the affections of the fathers of the Roman College. If he had, he would still be living gloriously in the world, he would not have fallen into trouble, he would be able to write on any subject he wished, even the rotation of the earth, and so forth." (Galilei, XVI, p. 117). This remark sounds so unlike Father Grienberger that it carries its lack of authenticity on its face. No doubt, some person ill-disposed toward the Jesuits in Rome carried this gossip with the deliberate purpose of presenting a Jesuit in a false light. Galileo, at the time, would have found no difficulty in believing it. The fair conclusion is that Grienberger was always sympathetic toward Galileo, and that he was even sympathetic toward Galileo's deduction of the Copernican system of the universe, but within the bounds of prudence.

51. Prince Cesi has preserved for us an episode in Schreck's ife shortly before his entry into the Jesuit novitiate. On August 20, 1611, Cesi, Schreck, and Lagalla were discussing Galileo's discoveries. The Prince and Lagalla argued against the Aristotelian theory of the necessary sphericity of the stars. Schreck was immovably pro-Aristotelian. "We were not strong enough," wrote Cesi, "to dislodge him from his conviction of the Peripatetic spherical perfection" (Galilei, XI, p. 174).

52. See Galilei, XI, p. 236.

53. *Ibid.*, p. 239.

54. *Ibid.*, p. 247.

55. *Geometria practica.*

56. See APGU, 529, f. 37r.

57. See APGU, 534, f. 57r. Reproduced in {Tacchi Venturi} *Alcune lettere lel P. Antonio Rubino*, 1900, pp. 13–14.

58. The "Perspettivi" are the masters in perspective, the art which teaches

how to draw or represent objects according to whether distance and position bring difference into their figure and form. Various errors of reading induced Tacchi Venturi to read "et si ita est veniant in esternum perspectivi, quia visionem fieri per extramissionem deffendunt" ({Tacchi Venturi}, *Alcune lettere*, p. 18).

59. See APGU, 534, ff. 55–56; reproduced in {Tacchi Venturi}, *Alcune lettere*, pp. 17–18.

60. *T'ien-wên lüeh* 天問略. *Problems of the Heavens: T'ien wên* 天問 is the title of a small poem by Ch'ü Yüan 屈原 (d. about 288 B.C.) in which are raised problems about the origin of the universe and about the movements of the sun and moon. Compare Fung Yu-lan, *A History of Chinese Philosophy*, translated by Derk Bodde (Princeton, 1952), I, p. 176.

61. Professor Gabrieli, *I Lincei e la Cina*, in *Rendiconti* of the Royal Academy of the Lincei, Class of Moral, Historical, and Philological Sciences, series VI, vol. XII (Rome, 1936), p. 246, believed that in this passage Diaz named Galileo under the Chinese phonetization Kia-li-lio. His source was Bernard (*Galilée et les Jésuites*, in *Revue des Questions Scientifiques* (Brussels, 1935), vol. 108, p. 374) who affirms the same. Bernard's source was Pfister, *Notices biographiques et bibliographiques sur les Jésuites de l'ancienne mission de Chine* (Shanghai, 1932), p. 110, who gives the equivalence Kia-li-lio 伽離略. Pfister's source was Wylie, *Notes on Chinese Literature* (1867), p. 108, who gives the characters used by Pfister. Evidently none of these authors took the trouble to consult Diaz's book. The first author, who wrote in Rome, and who did not know Chinese, is excusable. Not so the other three, who wrote in China. Actually the name of Galileo Galilei is never met with in Chinese books before the years 1637–1640, as we shall see below (Chapter 29). Particularly his name is not found in Diaz, *The Sphere*, although this work treats of Galileo. His name is not found in the edition of Diaz's work which appears in the *First Collection of Christian Books: [T'ien-hsüeh ch'u han]* 天學初函 (1629). And his name is not found in the edition of Diaz's work which the lamented Professor Pelliot regarded as the *editio princeps* (Vatican Library, Borgia Cinese, 324²⁵). This latter edition is of September 1615, according to the author's preface. The Vatican edition, indeed, possesses some particulars which the other editions do not have. In the first place, since the work is in the form of questions and answers, this edition is the only one which indicates Emmanuel Diaz 陽瑪諾 as he who "answers" 條答 these questions, and gives the names of the two official revisers 參定 of the work, John da Rocha 羅如望 and Peter Ribeiro 黎寧石, who reached China respectively in 1597 and 1604. In the second place, it is also the only edition which gives the list of nine Chinese literati, all laymen, well known in the history of the Catholic Church in China in the neighborhood of 1600, who would have been the "proof readers" 全閱. They are: Chou Hsi-ling 周希令, K'ung Chên-shih 孔貞時, Wang Ying-hsiung 王應熊, Hsiung Ming-yü 熊明遇, Li Chih-tsao 李之藻, Hsü Lo-shan 許樂善, Yang T'ing-yün 楊廷筠, Hsü Kuang-ch'i 徐光啓, and Cho Êrh-k'ang 卓爾康. Among these, namely Li

Chih-tsao, Yang T'ing-yün, and Hsü Kuang-ch'i, in 1615 were already Christians, baptized respectively in 1610, 1611, and 1603, under the names Leo, Michael, and Paul. Compare D'Elia, II, p. 168, n. 3; III, p. 13, n. 3; II, p. 250, n. 3. The first three of the [other] six each made a preface to Diaz's work. That of K'ung Chên-shih is of May 1615, that of Wang Ying-hsiung instead is of April of the same year, while the third, that of Chou Hsi-ling, bears no date. Concerning these personages, of whom one or the other seems to have been baptized, compare D'Elia, II, p. 253, n. 3; III, p. 13, n. 2; p. 15, n. 1. Otherwise the text of all these editions is exactly the same, as also that of the three prefaces.

62. Chinese measure of length equaling 0.33 m.

63. Chinese itinerary measure variable according to time and place. Today it corresponds to 576 m, but in Diaz's day, to about 400 m. D'Elia, II, p. 22, n. 19. Diaz means about 25 kilometers.

64. Here the author draws an oval figure with two earlike appendages, the two stars which, according to Galileo, accompany Saturn. See Fig. 1.

65. Early in July 1610, Galileo discovered that Saturn was "three-bodied" and communicated this news to several Italian and German scientists, among them Clavius and Grienberger (Galilei, XIX, p. 611). About six months later, Clavius learned from Anthony Santini that Galileo said that Saturn was no longer " three-bodied," but was composed of three stars: one in the middle, one on each side. But Galileo also gave a third description of Saturn at about this same time. Observing from the Roman College, he said that Saturn was "oblong, like o○o" (Galilei, X, pp. 484–485). On April 24, 1611, Clavius, Grienberger, Van Maelcote, and Lembo replied to an inquiry about the matter from Cardinal Bellarmine. "We have observed that Saturn is not round like Jupiter and Mars, but is egg-shaped and oblong, like o○o. We have not, however, seen the two little stars on the sides sufficiently detached from the central body to decide whether the three stars are separate" (Galilei, XI, p. 93). Plainly this is the source upon which Diaz depended for his information about Saturn.

66. Following is the reply of the four professors of the Roman College to Cardinal Bellarmine, April 24, 1611: "One sees with Jupiter four stars which move very rapidly: sometimes all towards the east, sometimes all towards the west, sometimes some towards the east, sometimes some towards the west, in an almost straight line. They cannot be fixed stars because their motion is more rapid and different from that of the fixed stars, and they continually change their distance among one another and from Jupiter" (Galilei, XI, p. 93).

67. See D'Elia, I, p. 181, n. 1.

68. See chapter 4.

69. *Ta-hsi Li-hsi-t'ai hsien-shêng hsing-chi* 大西利西泰先生行蹟.

70. For P. Van Spiere, compare Joseph Masson, *Missionnaires belges sous l'ancien régime* 1500–1800; I, *Ceux qui versèrent leur sang* (Brussels, 1947), pp. 84–95.

71. See D'Elia, III, p. 16, note *a*.

72. *Ibid.*, I, p. 385, n. 5.
73. *Ibid.*, II, p. 387, n. 3.
74. *Ibid.*, II, p. 250, n. 3.
75. *Ibid.*, II, p. 168, n. 3.
76. RASJ, *Jap.-Sin.*, 14, ff. 347v–348r.
77. See Tacchi Venturi, II, pp. 490–491.
78. RASJ, *Jap.-Sin.*, 113, f. 267r.
79. Born in Sernancelhe, diocese of Lamego, Portugal, in 1561. He went to Japan in 1576, where in December 1580 he entered the Society of Jesus. He was ordained priest at Macao in 1594, and he made his profession of the four vows in 1601. He was procurator of the Japanese mission from 1591 until 1626. But from 1614 he lived at Macao as a refugee from persecution. He should not be confused with John Rodriquez Girão or Giram (1558–1627?), also a missionary to Japan. See Schurhammer in *Archivum Historicum Societatis Iesu*, I (Rome, 1932), pp. 24–29.
80. RASJ, *Jap.-Sin.*, 15, f. 99v.
81. See D'Elia, I, p. clxxi, n. 2.
82. On July 23, 1611, he described the convocation and Galileo's recent discoveries to Father Jacob Van der Straeten, rector of Bruges. See Galilei, XI, pp. 162–163.
83. See "Civiltà Cattolica" (1923), III, p. 488, n. 2.
84. The former library of the Jesuits of Peking still conserves five of his works. See *Catalogue de la Bibliothèque du Pé-t'ang* (Peking 1949), NN. 2689–2694.
85. See Lamalle, *La propagande du P. Nicolas Trigault en faveur des missions de Chine* (1616), in *Archivum Historicum Societatis Iesu*, IX (Rome, 1940), p. 82.
86. *Ibid.*, p. 83.
87. *Ibid.* p. 87.
88. A year before his departure from Lisbon one of his disciples gave him a gift of a copy of Thomas Finck's *Geometriae rotundi Libri XIIII* (Basle {1583}) with this dedication by hand: "Et hanc rotundi geometriam clarissimo praeceptori P. Wenceslao Pantaleoni S.J. longinquae peregrinationis comitem libenter do dono. D. V. Noguera fr. S. J., discipulus studiosus. Olissipone, X Kal. Iunii 1617." ["And this geometry of the round I gladly give in gift to the most illustrious preceptor Father Wenceslaus Pantaleon S.J. as a companion on a distant sojourn abroad. D.V. Noguera brother S.J., zealous disciple. At Lisbon, 23 May 1617."] See *Catalogue de la Bibliothèque du Pé-t'ang*, N. 1608.
89. Compare Väth, *Johann Adam Schall von Bell* (Cologne, 1933), pp. 40–42.
90. [Copernicus, *Concerning the Revolutions of the Heavenly Orbs* (*De revolutionibus orbium coelestium;* Nuremberg, 1543), divided into 6 books.]
91. See APGU, 534, f. 83r.
92. "Impendit in hanc rem non segnem, ut video, operam P. Christophorus Scheinerus, quem mihi Reverentia Vestra suis literis et laudaverat et commen-

daverat; verum illi nondum ob occupationes scribere licuit. Theses ipsius necdum videram, comparavi tamen ocius, ubi illum edidisse, Reverentia Vestra scribente, cognovi. Non displicet libellus" (APGU, 534, f. 90r.). ["Father Christopher Scheiner gives timely attention, as I see, to this affair (i.e., the difficulties raised by the recent astronomical discoveries) whom Your Reverence has praised and commended to me for his learning. Really, I have been too busy to write to him. And I had not seen his propositions. But as soon as Your Reverence wrote I quickly procured (his works) at the place where you said they were published, and I have become acquainted (with his thought). The little book is not displeasing."]

93. See APGU, 534, f. 90r.

94. [Translators' note: our translation has been substituted for D'Elia's paraphrase].

95. See Chapter 7, "The Link Connecting Galileo with China;" and Chapter 10, "Galileo Jokes about the Novice, Schreck."

96. See "Aevum" (Milan, 1932), VI, p. 516.

97. "Miror D. Galilaeum urgere tantopere motum terrae. An non satis esset dicere sit hypothesis ad calculum astronomicum iuvandum, quicquid sit de ipsa veritate. Magno certe meo incommodo edictum prodiit; sic enim exactum calculum eclipsium ab ipso pro Sinensibus expectare non licet. Videat tamen apud Principem {Cesi} utrum ab ipso Galilaeo pro nostris usibus obtineri posset; pollicebor silentium quibusvis conditionibus; inquirat utrum exactum habeat illum calculum, an multis differat a Tychonico" (Gabrieli, p. 564). ["I marvel at Mr. Galileo for urging so earnestly the motion of the earth. In my opinion it is not sufficient to say that it is a hypothesis useful in astronomical calculation, no matter what the truth is. Certainly the edict has come as a great inconvenience to me. Now I shall not expect the calculation of eclipses which I requested from him in the interests of the Chinese. Inquire of Prince (Cesi), however, whether the calculation is obtainable from Galileo for our use. I promise silence under all conditions. Find out whether that calculation is exact, or whether it differs much from the Tychonic."]

98. "A Domino Galilaeo unice optarem modum computandi eclipses solis et lunae, idest hypothesim solis et lunae ante meum ad Sinas abitum; nam procul dubio habebit calceolum longe exactiorem quam Tycho. Ea de re moneat illustrissimum Principem {Cesi} an aliqua spes sit, et si non esset, an saltem mihi abeunti communicare velit, sub quavis obligatione, ob publicum religionis apud Sinas propagandae bonum. Saltem dicat unam vel alteram eclipsim sequentis anni, ut videam quantum distet a calculo Tyconis vel Remi nostri" (Gabrieli, p. 569).

99. "Salutet officiosissime Principem Caesium . . . per quem admodum opto ut suo tempore ante abitum nostrum ex Europa aliquid a Galilaeo obtineat quod nostris Sinis ad computum eclipsium inservire possit" (Gabrieli, p. 571).

100. Compare Gabrieli, p. 581. On May 1, 1616, Faber gave to Father

Nicholas Trigault and to Schreck "amicis dulcissimis" ["very dear friends"] a copy of the *Nautica Mediterranea* by Bartholomew Crescenzio, printed at Rome in 1601, accompanying the gift with these Latin verses:

Ito, redito vias iterum, felicibus astris,
Sinarum ignotis tu solus nuper ab oris,
Ex sociis, Christi spargunt qui semina in agro
Gentili, nostrum rediisti primus in orbem;
Care Deo, dilecte mihi, sic itur ad astra.
Salve Christiadum Genitor, Nicolae, minister
Verbi operisque Dei, cari fac cura{?} sodalis,
Dimidii vitae nostrae, quem ducis ad Indos.
Sit tibi; neu capiat vos vestri oblivio Fabri,
Si quando aeterni libatis sacra Tonanti.
[Go back, go back again under the felicitous stars
You who recently from the unknown lands of the Chinese
Were the first and only one to return to our world
From comrades (Jesuits) who are scattering seed in
the field of the Gentile.
O dear to God, precious to me, such is the way of
the stars.
Hail, O Nicholas, begetter of Christians,
minister
Of the Word and work of God, see to it that you
take care of the dear comrade,
The half of our life, whom you lead to the Indies.
Let him be yours; nor let forgetfulness of
your Faber take hold of (either of) you
Whenever you make libations to the eternal
Thunderer.]
See *Catalogue de la Bibliothèque du Pé-t'ang*, N. 3254.

101. See Gabrieli, p. 630.
102. See Lamalle, *art. cit.*, *Archivum Historicum Societatis Iesu*, IX (1940), p. 75.
103. As I have pointed out in my article *Le "Generalità sulle Scienze Occidentali" di Giulio Aleni* (p. 62, n. 3), published in the *Rivista degli Studi Orientali* of the University of Rome (Rome, 1950), XXV, pp. 58–76, this is the constant figure in Chinese sources towards the years 1620–1630. Dr. Michael Yang T'ing-yün 楊廷筠 (about whom see D'Elia, III, p. 13, n. 3) in his *Treatise of Answers to Doubts: Tai i pien* 代疑編 (1621) thus expresses himself: "After Matthew Ricci came as a guest to {our} country and received sustenance in life and burial in death, his Sovereign {=the Pope}, wishing to extend his thanks in gratitude, sent expressly his subject Nicholas Trigault to present tribute. Besides local products there were more than 7000 illustrated, bound

books, not counting duplicates and small pamphlets. The boxes of books have already arrived at Macao, and they expect that one day they will be presented at court." He repeated the same two years later in Julius Aleni's *Generality in the Occidental Sciences: Hsi Hsüeh fan* 西學凡. There he wrote: "More than 7000 volumes of works relating to the six divisions have already arrived *via* the sea, and all would merit being translated . . . If I had ten years before me, and about ten or more collaborators, I should do it." The same figure is given also by Dr. Leo Li Chih-tsao 李之藻 (about whom see D'Elia, II, p. 168. n. 3) in 1623 in the *Preface* to Aleni's *Geography of Non-tributary Countries: Chih-fang wai chi* 職方外紀, where he writes: "Dr. Trigault has brought more than 7000 volumes of his kingdoms as tribute, to make thereof a library where one can consult the science of oriental and occidental sages." In that same year 1623 he repeated the same, writing in the *Preface* to Julius Aleni's *Generality in the Occidental Sciences:* "In these last years there have arrived from the Occident 7000 volumes." Two years later in the *Epilogue* to Father Emmanuel Diaz the Younger's *Comment on the Nestorian Monument: Tu Ching-chiao pei shu-hou* 讀景教碑書後, he wrote again: "Commencing to translate the hidden sense and the great phrases of the 7000 volumes arrived by sea, we shall give to the books a glory which since antiquity they have never had. It is like a street which one cannot traverse in vain. Here is why we have waited up until today." In 1627 Dr. Philip Wang Chêng 王徵 (about whom see D'Elia, II, p. 593, n. 1), translating the first European book into Chinese under the title *Illustrated Explanation of the Instruments of Mechanics: Ch'i ch'i t'u shuo* 奇器圖説, with the concourse of Father John Schreck, said in the *Preface:* "The *Illustrated Explanation of the Instruments of Mechanics* is one of the illustrated books brought by the literati of the Far West, one of the more than 7000." Finally, in 1629, Li Chih-tsao in the general *Preface* to the *First Collection of Christian Books: T'ien-hsüeh ch'u han* 天學初函 wrote: "In these last years there have come from the Occident 7000 volumes." It is useless to prolong this list of texts which continue in the same manner for almost the whole of the seventeenth century. Who wants to see others may consult Fang Hao's *Seven Thousand European Books Brought to China by Nicholas Trigault in* 1620, in Fang Hao, pp. 1–14. This number, however, does not go without difficulty, as P. Verhaeren, C.M., points out in his interesting study, *Aperçu historique de la Bibliothèque du Pé-t'ang,* p. xii, placed as introduction to the *Catalogue de la Bibliothèque du Pé-t'ang* (Peking, 1949). But the solution which he proposes does not satisfy.

104. "Dominus Galilaeus de Galilaeis nihil gratius posset praestare missioni sinensi, quam si mitteret suam theoriam solis et lunae sine tabulis: id enim expectant a nobis avide Sinae, ut demus certiorem eclipsium calculum quam ipsi habeant. Tychonicus bonus est, errat tamen aliquando uno quadrante. Quod si mediante illustrissimo Principe Caesio . . . id fieri posset, ternarius benefactor missionis sinensis accederet" (Gabrieli, p. 747).

105. "A Galileo, ut etiam alias scripsi, summopere exoptarem calculum eclypsium, praesertim solarium, ex suis novis observationibus; nam iste nobis

est summe necessarius ad emendationem calendarii; et si quis sit titulus quo niti possimus, ne nos pellant toto regno, solus est iste. Princeps Caesius sine dubio ab illo impetrare posset. Forte etiam ipsa Archiducissa Florentiae, si de hac re moneretur a fratre Imperatore vel Leopoldo. Sed vereor ne hae turbae Europae ad alia omnia intentos ita eos occupent, ut non sit consultum de hac recula eos monere. Silentium porro spondeo, et autori debitum honorem. Non enim mihi in hoc genere quidquam arrogo, et libenter aliorum laudo in quavis scientia industriam" (Gabrieli, *Giovanni Schreck Linceo*, in *Rendiconti* of the Royal National Academy of the Lincei, Class of Moral, Historical, and Philological Studies, series VI, vol. XII (Rome, 1937), p. 502).

106. Faber wrote to Cesi on February 20, 1624: "The said Mr. Virginius {Cesarini}, Lincean, has read Father Terrentius' letter and thinks it a good idea to have Mr. Galileo favor Father Terrentius with his calculation of eclipses" (Galilei, XIII, p. 166).

107. On March 8, 1624, that is, three weeks after the preceding attempt, Faber wrote to Cesi: "I have begged {Mr. Marius Guiducci} for the observations desired by Father Terrentius. Marius thinks that Mr. Galileo will comply" (Galilei, XIII, p. 168).

108. See Gabrieli, p. 875.

109. See Gabrieli, *I Lincei e la Cina*, p. 252.

110. With the exception of the personal controversy about priority in the discovery of sunspots, Father Scheiner did not oppose Galileo. For instance, he did not oppose him on the basic question of the Copernican system. Shortly before January 10, 1626, ten years after the injunction of the Holy Office, he told Faber that he admitted Galileo's opinion concerning the system of the universe (Galilei, XIII, p. 300). Even after Galileo's second condemnation, in 1633, Scheiner, according to Father Athanasius Kircher's testimony cited above, conformed to the Ptolemaic system in his publications only "by force and obedience." Such also was Descartes's impression after reading Scheiner's books. Descartes wrote in February 1634: "Je ne scaurois croire que le Scheiner mesme en son âme ne croie l'opinion de Copernic" (Galilei, XVI, p. 56). ["I do not know that Scheiner himself, in his heart, does not believe the opinion of Copernicus"—that is, "I suspect that he does believe it."]

111. See Gabrieli, *Giovanni Schreck*, p. 510.

112. Schreck's letter to the mathematicians of Ingolstadt and Kepler's reply are published in *Kepleri Opera Omnia*, VII, pp. 667–681.

113. [See *The Book of Psalms*, King James version, II, 8.]

114. They are the *Tabulae Rudolphinae quibus astronomicae scientiae . . . restauratio continetur*, 1627. See *Catalogue de la Bibliothèque du Pé-t'ang*, N. 1902.

115. Compare *Catalogue de la Bibliothèque du Pé-t'ang*, N. 2151. This observation is from Bernard in his article *L'Encyclopédie astronomique du P. Schall*, in *Monumenta Serica* (Peking, 1937–1938), III, p. 67. It is not possible, however, to admit with him that when Rho in 1633 made use for the first time of logarithms we can attribute the merit for this to the works of Kepler "sans courir

le risque de beaucoup nous tromper" (*ibid.*) ["without running the risk of being very much mistaken".] Meanwhile the fact is that there is not only risk but error itself. Rho's preface to his treatise on the *Napierian Calculus* 籌算, of which there is a copy in the Vatican Library (General Collection, Orient. III, 235⁷), bears the date April 23, 1628, when most certainly in China there had not been received Kepler's works. Father Rho translated instead, probably through the Latin translation *De proportionum instrumento invento* (Strassburg, 1612), (of which a copy is in the former Library of the Jesuits of Peking; see *Catalogue de la Bibliothèque du Pé-t'ang*, N. 1655), a work of Galileo the original Italian title of which was *Le Operazioni del compasso geometrico et militare* (Padua, 1606). The Chinese translation had the title *The Proportional Compass: Pi-li-kuei-ch'ih* 比例規尺, and probably does not differ from Rho's other work, *Explanation of the Proportional Compass: Pi-li-kuei chieh* 比例規解, of which the Vatican Library possesses two copies (*Borgia Cinese*, 318, int. 1, and *General Collection, Orient.* III, 235, int. 6).

116. He was born at Hangchow or Wulin, had the agnomen [Jan-chên] 然眞, and died in 1665.

117. *Telescopium: sive ars perficiendi novum illud Galilaei visorium instrumentum ad sydera.*

118. 舊宿中北星.

119. Compare Schall, *The Telescope: Yüan-ching shuo* 遠鏡説.

120. *Yüan Hsi ch'i ch'i t'u shuo lu* 遠西奇器圖説録.

121. See the Chinese text in Fang Hao, p. 293.

122. 至于天漢斜絡天體, 古昔多謬解. 邇來窺以遠鏡知是無算小星接攢一帶即如積尸氣等, 亦小星攢聚以成, 第非目所能辨, 遂作如是觀耳.
Introduction to the {European} Calendar: Li yin 曆引 ff. 12b–13a.

123.
至若用遠鏡以窺
衆星較多于平時.
不啻數十倍而且
耀㷍然.

The Fixed Stars and the Guide to the Calendar: Hêng hsing li chih 恒星曆指, *chüan* 3, f. 39b.

124. *Theory of the Five Planets and Guide to the Calendar: Wu wei li chih* 五緯曆指, *chüan* 1, ff. 32a–36a. This *Theory* ought, naturally, to be before the author's death (1638), and after the year 1636, which is mentioned in *chüan* 9, f. 28b. We can, thus, date it as of the year 1637 without danger of making a mistake.

125. *Ibid.*, *chüan* 3, f. 41 a–b.

126. *Ts'ê t'ien yüeh shuo* 測天約説.

127. 從前所論, 皆爲臆説也.

128. 獨西方之國, 近歲有度數名家, 造爲望遠之鏡, 以測太白. 則有時晦, 有時光滿, 有時爲上下弦. 計太白附日而行. 遠時, 僅得象限之半, 與月異理, 因悟時在日上. 故光滿而體微. 若地日星參直, 則不可見. 稍遠而猶在上, 則若幾望之月也. 時在日下, 則晦. 三參直, 故晦. 稍遠而猶在下. 若復蘇之月, 體微而光耀煜 {probably 煜}

然. 在旁, 故為上下弦也. 辰星體小, 去日更近, 難見其晦明, 因其運行不異太白, 度亦與之同理. John Schreck, S.J., *The Sphere* (c. 1628), 上, c. I, ff. 16b–17a. There is a copy in RASJ, *Jap.-Sin.*, II, 50.

129. 太陽面上有黑子, 或一, 或二, 或三, 四而止, 或大, 或小, 恒于太陽東西徑上行, 其道止一線, 行十四日而盡. 前者盡, 則後者繼之. 其大者能減太陽之光. 先時或疑為金水二星, 考其躔度則又不合. 近有望遠鏡, 乃知其體不與日體為一, 又不若雲霞之去日極遠, 特在其面. 而不審為何物. John Schreck, *The Sphere*, 下, c. II, f. 15b.

130. See *The Works of Hsü Kuang-ch'i with Additions: Tsêng ting Hsü Wên-ting kung chi* 增訂徐文定公集 c. IV, p. 22; Schall, *The Origin of the Commission of the Calendar: Chih-li yüan-ch'i* 治曆緣起 (in RASJ, *Jap.-Sin.*, II, 15) c. I, f. 1a; Bernard, *L'Encyclopédie astronomique du P. Schall:* in *Monumenta Serica*, III (1937–38), pp. 71–72.

131. "窺筩眼鏡." Compare Schall, *The Origin of the Commission of the Calendar*, f. 69b.

132. Compare Fang Hao, p. 294.

133. *Shigaku zasshi* 史學雜誌.

134. The citation is incorrect and the incorrectness probably arises from the slight erudition of the person who put Rodriguez's letter into Chinese. The exact citation, extracted from gloss XI, *Hsi-tz'ŭ shang ch'uan* 繫辭上傳, of the *Book of Changes: I ching* 易經, is:

易有太極, 是生兩儀, 兩儀生四象四象生八卦

i.e.: "In the transformation there was the Supreme Ultimate, which produced the two forms, which produced the four images, which in their turn produced the eight trigrams." See Forke, *Geschichte der alten chinesischen Philosophie* (Hamburg, 1927), p. 171. The Supreme Ultimate, symbolized by a point, indicates the Primordial Principle or the Ultimate Cause. The two forms, represented by two lines, one whole and the other broken, are the positive principle Yang 陽 and the negative principle Yin 陰, to which allusion is made here for the first time in the whole of Chinese literature. The four images are the four possibilities of combination of a whole line and a broken line, or the four bigrams. The eight possible combinations of these four bigrams give the eight trigrams. Legge (*The Yi King*, in Max Müller, *The Sacred Books of the East*, XVI, p. 12,373) suspects that this text, coming from a Taoistic source of the V–IV century B.C., may have infiltrated this book of the Confucian school.

135. For Matthew Ricci the Great Ultimate is the *materia prima* of the Scholastics. See D'Elia, II, p. 297, note *b* sqq.

136. The three principal duties are those of subject to sovereign, of son to father, and of wife to husband. The five ordinary virtues are: benevolence, righteousness, politeness, wisdom, and fidelity. The five social relations are those between sovereign and subject, father and son, elder and younger brother, husband and wife, and friend and friend. See Mayers, *The Chinese Reader's Manual*, pp. 317, 332, 337.

137. The Chinese text of this letter has been reproduced by Fang Hao, pp. 216–217, and the present translation is based on this text.

138. *Ch'ien k'un t'i i* 乾坤體義. Compare D'Elia, II, p. 52, n. 3.

139. See note 60.

140. See note 126.

141. 千里鏡.

142. See Fang Hao, p. 294.

143. According to *The Precious Mirror of the Present Dynasty* 國朝寶鑑, translated by W. Carl Rufus, *Astronomy in Korea*, in *Transactions of the Korean, Branch of the Royal Asiatic Society*, 1926, vol. 26, p. 36. I take this information from Bernard, note 130, p. 446.

144. See Yoshio Mikami, *The Development of the Mathematics in China and Japan* (Leipzig, 1913), pp. 158–165.

145. See Fang Hao, p. 294.

146. *Ta k'o wên* 答客問. See Fang Hao, p. 294.

147. See my article *The Double Stellar Hemisphere of Johann Schall von Bell, S.J.* (*Peking, 1634*) in *Monumenta Serica*, 1959, XVIII, pp. 328–359.

148. *Hsin fa li yin* 新法曆引.

149. *Hsin fa piao i* 新法表異.

150. The Chinese written language, which is distinct from the Chinese spoken language, is so difficult that Westerners who have successfully written even a slight work correctly and elegantly are to be counted on the fingers of one hand, if they are to be counted at all. The greatest sinologists, including Ricci among the ancients and Zottoli among the moderns, have written their books, at least those of any length, with the aid of a Chinese secretary. Often they dictated and explained in the spoken Mandarin dialect what the scribe wrote down in fine literary style. In fact, in most cases Chinese books by ancient missionaries carry two names: the name of the European missionary, Ricci, Schall, Verbiest, and so forth, to whom is attributed the oral dictation of the work; and the name of the Chinese literatus who did the writing, or, at least, who "corrected the proof," by which is meant something more than the simple mechanical labor of correcting typographical errors. Excellent literati, imperial academicians, and ministers of state, even though pagans, took pleasure in putting into elegant style what the missionaries explained to them about science and religion. See D'Elia, II, p. 283, n. 5.

151. *The Fixed Stars and Guide to the Calendar*, *chüan* 3, f. 41 *a–b*. [Rho based much of his book on Schall's book. Note the similarity between this statement and that at note 125.]

152. *Divergences of European Astronomy from Chinese Astronomy*, *chüan* 下, f. 20 *a*.

153. See note 147.

154. Born at Wuchiao in Hopeh, obtained the licentiate in 1603, the doctorate ten years later. He was first director of schools at Kaifeng in Honan, then prefect of Tsinan in Shantung, then provincial judge of Shensi. Presented to court by Hsü Kuang-ch'i, at the death of the latter he succeeded him as head of the Bureau of the Calendar and remained there for ten years (1634–1644).

It was under him that in 1635 there was finished the collection of Chinese books on the New Astronomy in 137 *chüan*, besides two tables. After which the Astronomical Bureau busied itself with the manufacture of astronomical instruments, such as quadrants, globes, telescopes, etc. Compare Arthur W. Hummel, Editor, *Eminent Chinese of the Ch'ing Period* (Washington, D.C., 1943), I, pp. 488–489.

155. 窺管創自遠西, 乃新法中儀器之一, 所以佐諸儀之所不及. 為用最大. 此輔臣原題工製一具. 待升晷, 星晷造完, 并進〇前者也...

夫此窺管之制, 論其圓徑, 不過寸許. 而上透星光, 注於人目. 凡兩星密聯, 人目難別其界者, 正管 ‖ 能別之. 凡星體細微, 人目難見其體者, 此管能見之. 又凡兩星距半度以內, 新法所謂三十分, 窮儀器與目力不能測見分明者, 此管能兩納其星於中, 而明晰之, 是其容半度強者, 即此官之度分是也. 惟兩星相距半度以外, 則不能同見.

臣請畧舉一二. 如觜宿三星相距三十七分, 不能同見. 五車西柱下二星相距四十四分愈, 不能同見. 則此管之度分為半度強, 不其彰明較著乎.

故臣於閏八月二十五夜及九月初一 ‖ 夜, 同部監諸臣, 在局仰見木星在鬼宿之中, 距積尸僅半度, 因木星光大, 氣體不顯, 舍窺管, 別無可測.

臣是以獨用此管, 令人人各自窺視, 便明見積尸為數十小星團聚, 又能見木星與積尸共納於一管, 則其相犯為不惧...

156. 崇禎七年九月十三日具題, 本月十六日奉 ‖ 〇旨, 窺管僅儀器之一, 佐諸儀所不及, 知道了, 俟製完進覽, 禮部知道. Schall, *The Origin of the Commision of the Calendar*, ff. 142b–145a.

157. 夫窺筒亦名望遠鏡, 前奉明間業已約畧陳之. 但其制, 兩端俱有玻璃, 而其中層叠虛管, 隨視物遠近, 以為短長, 亦有引伸之法. 不但可以仰窺天象, 且能映萬里外物, 如在目前. 可以望敵施砲, 有大用焉. 此則遠西諸臣羅雅谷, 湯若望, 等, 從其本國, 携來而葺飾之以 ‖ 呈〇覽者也...

崇禎七年十月二十九日具題, 十一月初三日奉〇旨, 擇吉撥給人夫, 恭進窺筒着, 先進覽該衙門知道. Schall, *The Origin of the Commission of the Calendar*, ff. 151a–152b.

158. ...臣随於本月初 ‖ 五日會同內臣盧維寧, 魏國徵到局驗, 看窺筒遠鏡, 其間引伸之法, 窺視之宜, 臣已與二臣詳言之矣. 謹將窺筒遠鏡一具, 遵旨先進〇覽, 伏乞〇覽.

計開, 窺筒遠鏡一具, 托鏡銅器二件, 錦袱一件, 黃綾鏡條一具, ‖ 木架一座.

159. Compare Schall, *The Origin of the Commission of the Calendar*, ff. 153a–154b. Väth, *Johann Adam Schall von Bell*, Cologne, 1933, p. 105, misled no doubt by Father Van Hée, assigned this act to February 2, 1634. The official Chinese document, however, bears the date I have assigned to it.

160. 窺遠鏡二具, 托鏡銅器各二件, 黃綾鏡條二具, 木架二座.
Compare Schall, *The Origin of the Commission of the Calendar*, f. 193a–b.

161. The annual letter of 1637 (RASJ, Jap.-Sin., 115, II, f. 385) informs us that at various intervals Schall and Rho presented clocks to the emperor "e canuchales que o Emperador estimou muito" ["and telescopes which the emperor esteemed highly."]

162. Compare Peter Huang Fei-mo 黃斐默 *In Praise of the True Religion: Chêng chiao fêng pao* 正教奉褒, I, f. 16a.

163. Concerning him, compare Pfister, *Notes biographiques et bibliographiques sur les Jésuites de l'ancienne Mission de Chine* (Shanghai, 1932–1934), pp. 136–

143.
164. *Hsing p'ing* 星屛.
165. *Yü p'ing* 輿屛.
166. See Peter Huang Fei-mo, *ibid.* I, ff. 17–18.
167. 曆法西傳.
168. A few years before 1540, only once did I see Galileo's name phoneticized, by Rho in his work *Theory of the Five Planets and Guide to the Calendar, chüan* 9, f. 14b, apropos of light, under the form *Chia-li-lou* 加利婁, where only the last character does not correspond to Schall's last two. The latter, therefore, reproduces better the Italian sounds *le-o*.
169. 第谷沒後, 望遠鏡出, 天象微妙盡著. 于是有加利勒阿, 于三十年前, 創有新圖, 發千古星學之所未發, 著書一部. 自後名賢繼起, 著作轉多. 乃知木星旁有小星四, 其行甚疾, 土星旁亦有小星二, 金星有上下弦, 等象, 皆前此所未聞. 且西旅每行至北極出地八十度, 即冬季為一夜, 又嘗周行大地, 至南極出地四十餘度, 即南極星盡見. 所以星圖記載獨全.　Schall, *History of Occidental Astronomers: Li-fa hsi chuan* (Vatican Library, General Collection. Orient. III. 244²), f. 12a. This book was published after these other three 月離曆指, 交食曆指, 五緯曆指, which are cited, and fiftythree years after Tycho Brahe had spoken of the meridians of more than a hundred stars (ff. 9a–12a).
170. Vol. XXXVIII, 1947–1949, pp. 321–329.
171. *Ibid.*, p. 328.
172. See Galilei, XII, pp. 171–172. See *ibid.*, XIX, p. 339.
173. See above, chapter 6, note 39; chapter 9, note 50; chapter 21, note 110.
174. See chapter 18.
175. See *Catalogue de la Bibliothèque du Pé-t'ang*, no. 1902.
176. See Wylie, *Notes on Chinese Literature* (Shanghai, 1922), p. 111.
177. See Fang Hao, p. 289.
178 問宗動天之行若何. 曰, 其説有二. 或曰. 宗動天, 非日一周天, 左旋于地, 內挈諸大, 與俱西也. 今在地面以上, 見諸星左行, 亦非星之本行. 盍星無晝夜一周之行, 而地及氣火通為一球, 自西徂東, 日一周耳.
　　如人行船, 具岸樹等, 不覺已行, 而覺岸行, 地以上人, 見諸星之西行, 理亦如此. 是則以地之一行, 免天上之多行, 以地之小周, 免天上之大周也.
　　然古今諸士, 又以為實非正解, 盍地為諸天之心, 心如樞軸, 定是不動, 且在船如見岸行曷不許在岸者得見船行乎. 其所取譬, 仍非確證.
　　正解曰, 地體不動, 宗動天為諸星最上大球, 自有本極, 自有本行, 而向內諸天, 其各兩極, 皆囿于宗動天中, 不得不與偕行. 如人行船中, 蟻行磨上, 自有本行, 又不得不隨船磨行也.
　　求宗動天之厚薄, 及其體其色等, 及諸天體色. 等, 自為物理之學, 不関曆學, 他書詳之, 如寰有詮等, 曆家言有諸動天, 諸小輪, 諸不同心圈等, 皆以齊諸曜之行度而已. 匪能實見其然. 故有異同之説. 今但測算為本. 孰見孰非, 未須深論.
Theory of the Five Planets and Guide to the Calendar, chüan 1, ff. 7b–8b.
179. 古今無疑, 其不同者. 古曰五星之行, 皆以地心為本天之心.
　　今曰五星以太陽之體為心. 古曰各星自有本天, 重重包裹, 不能相通, 而天體皆為實體.
　　今曰諸圈能相入, 即能相通, 不得為實體. 古曰土木火星, 恒居太陽之外. 今曰火星有時在太陽之內.　*Ibid., chüan* 1, ff. 3b–4a.

180. 問古者諸家曰：天體為堅為實，為徹照，今法火星圈，割太陽之圈，得非明背昔賢之成法乎.

曰：自古以來，測候所急，追天為本，必所造之法，與密測所得畧無乖爽，乃為正法. 茍為不然，安得泥古而違天乎.

以事理論之，大抵古測稍粗，又以目所見為準則更粗；今測較古，其精十倍，又用遠鏡為準，其精百倍. 是以舍古從今，良非自作聰明，妄違迪哲. *Ibid.*, *chüan* 1, f. 6b.

181. Professor B. Szcześniak, *Notes on the Penetration of the Copernican Theory into China* (*Seventeenth-Nineteenth Century*) in *The Journal of the Royal Asiatic Society* (1945), pp. 30-38. The citation is to p. 36.

182. Diaz's text was known earlier (see note 61), but it had not even been translated.

183. See Galilei, XV, p. 273.

184. See *ibid.*, p. 141.

185. Exactly three months after this injunction, Cardinal Bellarmine, who was at that time a member of the Congregation of the Index took up the defense of Galileo, writing out with his own hand the following statement:

"We, Robert Cardinal Bellarmine, having understood that Mr. Galileo Galilei was calumniated, or charged with having abjured in our hand the doctrine of Copernicus about the earth's motion and the sun's immobility, and also with having, therefore, done penance of a salutary kind, and we engaging in an investigation of the truth, say that the above-named Mr. Galileo has not abjured in our hand, nor in that of others according to our knowledge, the doctrine of Copernicus, neither here in Rome nor elsewhere according to our knowledge, any of his opinions or doctrines, nor even has received salutary penance or any other kind; but only was advised of the declaration made by our lord {the Pope} and published by the Congregation of the Index, in which it is contained that the doctrine attributed to Copernicus that the earth moves around the sun and that the sun is in the center of the world without moving from east to west, is contrary to Holy Scripture and on that account may not be defended or held. And in certification of this we have written and signed the present [statement] with our own hand. This day May 26, 1616. (Vatican Archives, *Miscellanea Arm.* X, 204, *Processo di Galileo Galilei.* f. 88, formerly 79 and 423.)

APPENDIX

1. See chapter 15.

2. See D'Elia, *Il contributo dei missionari cattolici alla scambievole conoscenza della Cina e dell' Europa*, in *Le Missioni cattoliche e la cultura dell' Oriente* (Rome, 1943), pp. 27–109, especially pp. 81–106.

3. See D'Elia, II, p. 387, n. 3, for more biographical data.

4. See D'Elia, I, p. 165, n. 3.

5. See D'Elia, II, p. 256, n. 4.

6. [Translators' note: The original Portuguese text of this document was first published together with its Italian translation in the original Italian edition of the present work. We have not reproduced the Portuguese text, and the English translation which follows is based upon D'Elia's Italian translation. In regard to the Portuguese text D'Elia says in a footnote (p. 73): "This report is preserved in RASJ, *Jap.-Sin.*, 113, ff. 283*v*–290*r*. It is authenticated by an autograph of Longobardo, then superior of the whole mission in China. This autograph appears at the beginning of the document (f. 283)." D'Elia, in this same footnote, then gives the autograph in Portuguese with its Italian translation in a parallel column. English translation: "A short account of the Chinese calendar and its errors, for which correction is desired, for presentation to Father Francis Pasio, Jesuit, Visitor to China and Japan, resident at Macao. China, 1612. From Peking. Work of Father Sabatino De Ursis."]

7. In the following pages all Chinese characters are supplied by D'Elia.

8. The dynastic histories always contain a few chapters which are concerned with the Chinese calendar. De Ursis must refer to the *History of the Yüan: Yüan shih* 元史. One might guess that he also saw the book: *Rules and Calendar of Today and Antiquity: Ku chin lü li k'ao* 古今律曆考 by the great astronomer Hsing Yün-lu 邢雲路. The latter was a native of Ansu in Kansu Province and received his doctorate in 1580. See *History of the Ming: Ming shih* 明史, c. 31, f.

11*b*. [Translators' note: Throughout this Appendix we have supplied romanizations for the titles of Chinese books.]

9. See D'Elia, II, p. 250, n. 3.

10. The most ancient Chinese calendar, consisting of parallel phrases with or without parallelism of ideas so characteristic of ancient Oriental literatures, must have formed originally an independent whole. Later it was put in the mouth of the semilegendary Emperor Yao and incorporated in chapter I of the *Book of History: Shu ching* 書經. This chapter is universally rejected by modern criticism. See Chavannes, *Les Mémoires historiques de Se-ma Ts'ien* (Paris, 1895), I p. 49, n. 1. But even if the chapter must be rejected and even if the calendar should not be put in the mouth of Yao, the scrap to which we allude may be regarded as authentic. It tells us of two persons: Hsi and Ho, and of four others, two of whom were the younger brothers of Hsi,

and the two younger brothers of Ho. These four were to occupy themselves with the four seasons. The two others had heaven and earth as their responsibility. Following are the words of this ancient calendar. The text I translate is from the *Historical Records: Shih chi* 史記 of Ssŭ-ma Ch'ien 司馬遷 (c. I) rather than from the *Book of History*, because the text in the former work is purer.

"Then {Yao} commanded Hsi and Ho carefully to observe the immense heavens and to apply methods of calculation to the sun, moon, constellations, and syzygy of conjunction, and then diligently to indicate the seasons to the people.

"In particular he commanded the second-born of Hsi to establish himself with the barbarians Yü 郁 {in the east} at a place called Valley of the Rising Sun 暘谷 in order carefully to follow the sun's rising and to determine and promulgate the labors of spring. The vernal equinox and the constellations of the birds {=α Hydrae} serve to regulate the middle of spring. The people in that season scatter {in the fields} and the birds and beasts suckle, or are small.

"Besides he commanded Hsi's youngest to establish himself in the south {Nan-chiao 南郊,} {at a place called Residence of Light 明都} in order to determine and promulgate the labors of summer and enable them with diligence to be completed. The summer solstice and the constellations of the fire {=π Scorpionis} serve to regulate the middle of summer. The people are exhausted and {the feathers and hair} of the birds and beasts become sparse, and change.

"Besides he commanded the second-born of Ho to establish himself in the western territory at a place called Valley of Obscurity 昧谷 in order carefully to follow the sun's setting and to determine and promulgate the works of fall. The autumnal equinox and the constellation of Aquarius {=β Aquarii} serve to regulate the middle of autumn. The people lead a tranquil and pacific life and the birds and beasts renew their feathers and hair.

"Besides he commanded the youngest of Ho to establish himself in a region of the north at a place called Residence of Darkness 幽都 in order to determine and observe hidden things. The winter solstice and the constellation of the Pleiades {=η Tauri} serve to determine the middle of winter. The people betake themselves to warmth {in houses} and the feathers and hair of the birds and beasts become very thick.

"The year has 366 days. By means of the intercalary moon one adjusts the four seasons.

"If all duties are regulated conformably to this, all labors will prosper." See Chavannes, *Mémoires*, I, pp. 43–49.

The number 3970 given by De Ursis is obtained by adding 1612, the year in which he wrote, to 2358, the first year {by anticipation} of Yao's reign, according to the conventional chronology which makes him reign between 2357 and 2255 B.C.

11. See D'Elia, *Antologia cinese* (Florence, 1944), pp. 78–81.

12. In 191 B.C., only 22 years after the Burning of the Books, Emperor Hui

惠 revoked the edict of Shih Huang-ti. The literati hastened then to recover the tablets which had escaped the fire and to take them to the great bibliophile Prince Hsien 獻王 (d. 129 B.C.) of Ho-chien 河間, brother of Emperor Wu. But another brother of the same emperor, Prince Kung 共王 of the country of Lu 魯, in the years 145–135 B.C., while tearing down a wall of the house of Confucius, found several other books written in "tadpole" 蝌蚪 characters. These tablets subsequently were arranged in order, at about the beginning of the Christian Era, by two great bibliophiles, father and son: Liu Hsiang 劉向 and Liu Hsin 劉歆. Thus, there came to be two collections for which we are indebted to two cousins: Tai the Elder 大戴 and Tai the Younger 小戴. In the first half of the second century A.D. the literatus Ma Yung 馬融 (79–166 A.D.) added to the collection of Tai the Younger three important chapters, of which one, *Rules of the Month: Yüeh ling* 月令 (See Couvreur, *Li Ki*, I, pp. 330–410), is another old calendar like that cited above, but relatively more recent and much more copious.

13. Ricci distinguishes clearly between "the judicial art," from the Spanish "arte judiciaria," which means astrology, "{the Chinese} thinking that all that happens in this inferior world depends upon the stars," and "the science of mathematics" received from the Mohammedans, who left to the Chinese only "the tables by which they calculate their year {=calendar} and eclipses of both luminaries and also the movements of the planets" (D'Elia, I, p. 41).

14. D'Elia, II, p. 168, n. 3.

15. D'Elia, I, pp. 41–42.

16. The *History of the Ming* (c. 31, f. 1b) counts 6 corrections from the twenty-fifth century to the third century B.C., 4 from the second century B.C. to the third century A.D., 15 from the third century to the sixth century, 15 from the seventh century to the tenth century, 17 from the tenth century to the thirteenth century, and 5 from the thirteenth to the fourteenth century, thus 62 in all.

17. See D'Elia, I, p. 41, n. 3; II, p. 56, n. 5.

18. Probably De Ursis alludes to the character 元 yüan=Tartar, which occurs in the name of Kublai Khan, an emperor of that period, or, to be more precise, in his reign title: Chih Yüan 至元 (1280–1294).

19. See D'Elia, I, p. 52, n. 2.

20. The two academicians who, with a Mohammedan, were commissioned by Hung Wu to translate these Arabic books in the autumn of 1382 were Li Ch'un 李狲 and Wu Pai-tsung 吳伯宗. The Chinese called the Mohammedan Ma-sha-i-hei 馬沙亦黑. See the *History of the Ming*, c. 37.Ma-sha-i-hei, also called Ma-i-ch'ih-hei 馬懿赤黑 was a Mongol who had remained in China after the fall of the Mongol dynasty, and occupied an important post in the Academy. He worked on the Sino-Mongol dictionary: *Hua i i-yü* 華夷譯語 for subjects, compiled in 1382. Compare *Bulletin of the School of Oriental and African Studies* (London, 1945), IX, p. 620, n. 1; p. 624. Also the other two (of whom the first was not Li Ch'un 李狲 but Li Yü-chung 李羽中) were Moham-

medans. All three of these Mussulmans in 1382 began the translation of the Moslem calendar. Compare *Bulletin de l'Université l'Aurore* (Shanghai, 1947), VIII, p. 405.

21. *Chi-ho yüan pên* 幾何原本. This translation was made between 1606 and 1607 and was printed probably in May of the latter year. See D'Elia, II, p. 358, n. 2.

22. This memorial was presented by Fan Shou-i 范守已, a native of Wei-ch'uan 洧川, Honan Province. He received his doctorate in 1574.

23. This memorial, presented by the astronomer Chou Tzǔ-yü 周子愚 (about whom see D'Elia, III, p. 16, note *a*), said: "Your subjects from afar, missionaries come from the Great Occident: Diego Pantoja, Sabatino De Ursis, and so forth, have brought mathematical books from their countries. Many of these books contain more than is in ours. Therefore, it is begged that what was done under Hung Wu in the translation of books from Western countries should now be repeated. That is to say, these astronomical experts, aided by members of the observatory, should be commissioned to translate these books and to repair what is missing in our books." See *History of the Ming*, c. 31, ff. 11 *a–b*.

24. These two astronomers were the above-mentioned Fan Shou-i (see "Errors in the calculation of the eclipse for December 15, 1610," note 22) and Hsing Yün-lu (see "Introduction: Purposes and sources of this essay," note 8).

25. Chinese silver money. See Yule-Burnell, *Hobson-Jobson, A Glossary of Colloquial Anglo-Indian Words and Phrases* (London, 1903), p. 888.

26. For this circle see D'Elia, *Il Mappamondo cinese del P. Matteo Ricci, S.I.* (Vatican City, 1938), p. 209, n. 138.

27. Since the Chinese hours are double, each corresponds approximately to two European hours. Thus, *tzǔ* 子 corresponds to the hours 23–1; *ch'ou* 丑 to 1–3; *yin* 寅 to 3–5. For the others see D'Elia, II, p. 99, n. 4. De Ursis in this passage considers the center of each double hour and therefore speaks of the hours 0, 2, and 4.

28. The three months with which the year at various times has been considered to begin by the Chinese are called the 三正. Under the Hsia 夏 Dynasty (*c.* 2100–*c.* 1600 B.C.) the year began the first month of spring 寅, called "the first month of man" 人正. Under the Shang-Yin 商殷 Dynasty (*c.* 1600–*c.* 1050 B.C.) the year began the twelfth month 丑, called "the first month of earth" 地正. Under the Chou 周 Dynasty (1050–249 B.C.) the year began the eleventh month 子, called "the first month of heaven" 天正. In 104 B.C. there was a return to the first month of spring as the beginning of the year, as under the Hsia. Compare J. Legge, *The Chinese Classics*, I, 1861, p. 162, note; III, Part I, p. 154, note.

29. See D'Elia, *Il Mappamondo cinese*, p. 201, n. 67.

30. See the preceding section, note 27.

31. The 10 " celestial trunks " 天干 (here represented by Roman numerals) and the 12 "terrestrial branches" 地支 (here represented by Arabic numerals) are

combined after this manner: I 1, II 2, III 3 . . . X 10, I 11, II 12, III 1, IV, 2, V 3 . . . X 12, forming a closed cycle of 60 called the "sexagesimal cycle." This cycle has been used in China for ages to calculate time: hours, days, months, and especially years. As we Europeans speak of the century of 100 years, the Chinese speak of a cycle of 60 years. Years, months, days, and hours thus are computed according to their place in the cycle, and each place is designated by a binomial formed by one character from the decimal series and one character from the duodenary series. If one knows the initial year of a given cycle, one can easily reconstruct a particular year with the aid of special tables. The current cycle began in 1924. According to some, it is the seventy-seventh, according to others the seventy-eighth. The first cycle, thus, would have begun in 2697 or 2637 B.C.

32. See L. Wieger, *Textes Historiques* (1929), I, p. 7; W.F. Mayers, *The Chinese Reader's Manual*, pp. 382-383.

33. See below, "Some peculiarities of the Chinese calendar."

34. See "The Chinese Zodiacal Constellations, with their Corresponding Elements and Animals, the Longitude of their Determinant Stars in A.D. 1800, and their Approximate Constellations," in Mathews, *A Chinese-English Dictionary* (Shanghai, 1931), p. 1177. The seven planets always recur according to this order: the sun 日, the moon 月, Mars 火, Mercury 水, Jupiter 木, Venus 金, Saturn 土, the sun 日, and so forth. Whence, one passes to the days of the week: Sunday, Monday, Tuesday, Wednesday, Thursday, Friday, Saturday, Sunday, and so forth.

35. These four signs correspond to the stars of the constellations as follows: the first corresponds to α, ι, τ (2), x, ν (2) Hydrae; the second corresponds to β, δ, π, ν, Scorpionis; the third corresponds to β Acquarii and α Herculis; the fourth corresponds to the Pleiades.

36. Here De Ursis mentions the great Chinese superstition about lucky 吉 and unlucky 凶 days deriving from geomancy 風水. See D'Elia, I, pp. 95-97.

37. See section "Epact and Golden Number."

38. The Chinese theory of the 5 elements: metal 金, wood 木, water 水, fire 火, and earth 土, known in antiquity, and given particular expression in the fourth century B.C., was used toward the beginning of the Christian Era to explain almost everything Chinese. In about 1599-1600, Matthew Ricci wrote and published at Nanking a small *Treatise on the Four Elements: Ssŭ yüan-hsing lun* 四元行論, the purpose of which was to combat the Chinese theory of the 5 elements. He rejected metal and wood to make place for air along with water, earth, and fire which the Chinese already included. See D.Elia, II, p. 51, n. 9; p. 52, n. 3.

39. The "nine ways" 九道 of the moon are: two black ways 黑道 on the north of the ecliptic; two red ways 赤道 (equinoxes) on the south of the ecliptic; two white ways 白道 on the west of the ecliptic; two blue ways 青道 on the east of the ecliptic; and one yellow way 黄道, the ecliptic itself. See Mayers, *Chinese Readers' Manual*, p. 365, n. 288.

40. See the diagram of the nine heavens in D'Elia, *Il Mappamondo cinese del P. Matteo Ricci S.I.* (Vatican City, 1938), plates III-IV, BEca.

41. See section "Origin of the calendar of the Ming Dynasty," note 17.

42. See sections "Epact and Golden Number" and "The solar cycle and Dominical Letter."

43. [The name given in the original Portuguese document is Yû hī. D'Elia points out that this name does not occur among the names of the emperors of China. However, I Hsi 義熙 (A.D. 405-418) existed; also two Yen Hsi: 延熹 (A.D. 158-166) and 延熙 (A.D. 238-257)].

44. See section "Origin of the calendar of the Ming Dynasty."

45. See section "The heavens and their movements according to the Chinese."

46. [Translators' note: De Ursis' estimate is about 10° too much. Since the longitude of Lisbon, measured from Greenwich, is about 9° 11'W. and that of Peking about 116° 28' E., the difference between the two cities is in fact approximately 125° 39'.]

47. See section "Establishment of a bureau of European astronomy."

INDEX

The asterisk (*) before page-numbers indicates that at these places Chinese characters are included in the citations.